# E X A M I N I N G
# FOOD TECHNOLOGY

to be returned on
...

# ANNE BARNETT

Heinemann Educational Publishers
Halley Court, Jordan Hill, Oxford OX2 8EJ
a division of Reed Educational & Professional Publishing Ltd

OXFORD  FLORENCE  PRAGUE  MADRID  ATHENS
MELBOURNE  AUCKLAND  KUALA LUMPUR  SINGAPORE  TOKYO
IBADAN  NAIROBI  KAMPALA  JOHANNESBURG  GABORONE
PORTSMOUTH NH (USA)  CHICAGO
MEXICO CITY  SAO PAULO

© Anne Barnett, 1996

First published 1996

00 99 98 97
10 9 8 7 6 5 4 3

**British Library Cataloguing in Publication Data**
A catalogue record for this book is available from the British
Library

ISBN 0 435 42062 3

Designed and produced by Gecko Ltd, Bicester, Oxon
Illustrated by Gecko Ltd
Cover illustration by Peter Byatt
Printed and bound in Great Britain by Bath Press Colourbooks,
Glasgow

**Acknowledgements**
The author would like thank: Clare Barnett-Thomas for typing the
manuscript and giving helpful advice; Julia and James Barnett for
their tireless consumption of ready meals; Roy Ballam and
Stephanie Valentine of the British Nutrition Foundation; Tony
Casdagli CBE of the British Federation of Bakers; Steve Charlton
of Mintel International Group Ltd; David Gregory; Flo Hadley HMI;
Alison Evenett; Georgina Lonsdale of the Flour Advisory Bureau
Ltd; Robert Morrell of the National Farmers' Union; Keith
Proudlove of the University of Humberside; Diana Ross of the
Public Health Laboratory Board; Carol Smith of the National Dairy
Council; Sally Tooth of the Chemical Industries Association;
Amon Trainer of APV Baker; Helen Atkinson, Keith Bashford, Laura
Brown, Gill Fine, Sara Gallagher, Brenda Jamieson, Alec Kyriakides
and Gerry Thomas, all of J. Sainsbury plc; Lynn Haywood and
Jenny Woolfe of the Ministry of Agriculture, Fisheries and Food;
Mr G.K. Noon MBE, Ashok Kaul and Tony McMullen of Noon
Products plc; Lee Gabot and Kelly Murphy of Tesco Stores Ltd;
the Institute of Food Science and Technology (UK); Pat Pawsey
and Jenny Tennet at the Upper Farm office for photocopying.

The publishers would like to thank the following for permission to
reproduce copyright material.
APV Baker for the redrawn illustration on p. 50 (the original pizza
plant featured was produced by APV Baker); British Nutrition
Foundation for the Dietary Reference Value tables on pp. 54–5,
from *Food – A Fact of Life: Energy and Nutrients* and the table of the
effects of temperature on food on p. 86; © 1985 A.G. Cameron
for the graph on p. 86 from *The Science of Food and Cooking* by Allan
Cameron, reproduced with permission of Hodder and Stoughton
Educational 1996; the Chemical Industries Association for the
ingredients lists on p. 115; © Giles Coren/Times Newspapers Ltd
for the article from *The Times*, 17 June 1996 on p. 113; CPC (UK)
Ltd for the HELLMANN'S Real Mayonnaise label on p. 70.
HELLMANN'S is a registered trademark of CPC International Inc,
reproduced by kind permission of CPC (UK) Ltd; Edward Brisco
Design for the Sainsbury recipe leaflet on p. 24, designed and
photographed by Edward Brisco Design; the Flour Advisory
Bureau for the redrawn illustration on p. 78 and for the text and
adapted flow diagram on p. 81, based on an illustration by Mr P.
Lamb, British Bakeries Ltd; the Health Education Authority for the
illustration on p. 52, © Health Education Authority, and the table
on p. 53, both from *The Balance of Good Health*; Diana Henry for the
'Thai grilled chicken' recipe on p. 24; HMSO for the bar chart on
p. 38, the data in the Dietary Reference Value tables on pp. 54–5,
the tables on pp. 57–8 , the table on p. 76, the bar charts on pp.
92ñ3 and the table on p. 93. Crown copyright is reproduced with
the permission of the Controller of HMSO; the National Dairy
Council for the bar chart from *Farm to Doorstep* on p. 38, the
redrawn illustration of a triglyceride on p. 56 and the adapted
illustration on p. 75; the Ministry of Agriculture, Fisheries and
Food for the mayonnaise label on p. 33 from Foodsense booklet
No. 3, *Understanding Food Labels*, PB 0553, © Crown copyright, and
the table on p. 34 from document CPDA/3 by the Food Labelling
and Standards division; Mintel International Group Ltd for the
figures for bread and morning goods on p. 93, from *Market
Intelligence*, March 1995; Anton Mosimann for the photograph of
the leek, potato and mozarella tart on p. 25; the Public Health
Laboratory Service for the map with figures and the graph on
p. 123, both from J.M. Cowden, P.G. Wall, G. Adak, H. Evans,
S. Le Baigue and D. Ross in 'Outbreaks of foodborne infectious
intestinal disease in England and Wales: 1992 and 1993' from
*Communicable Disease Report* 1995; 5: R 109-17; Penguin Books for
the table on p. 45, taken from *English Bread and Yeast Cookery* by
Elizabeth David, Penguin Books, (first published by Allen Lane,
1977) © Elizabeth David, 1977; Keith Proudlove for the diagram
on p. 11; J. Sainsbury plc for the information in the flow diagram
on p. 14, the recycle logo on p. 33, the healthy eating symbol on
pp. 33 and 52, the charts on p. 82, and the flow chart on p. 83;
Sodastream Ltd for the Traditional Style Ginger Beer label on
p. 65; the States of Jersey Department of Agriculture and
Fisheries for permission to reproduce both recipes and the
photograph of Tomato, Mozzarella and Basil Terrine on p. 25;
STUTE Foods Ltd for the marmalade label on p. 116; Taylors of
Harrogate for kindly supplying the tea and coffee odour library
information on p. 27 and the critical control point information on
p. 88; Tesco Stores Ltd for the flow diagram on p. 41 and the
sunflower oil label on p. 57; Van den Bergh Foods for the Flora
sunflower spread image on p. 56, reproduced by kind permission
of Flora; the World Health Organization for the tables on p. 84
and 87 and the adapted table on p. 80, all by F.L. Bryan in A *Guide
to Identifying Hazards and Assessing Risks Asociated With Food Preparation
and Service*.

The publishers would like to thank the following for permission to
use photographs.
APV Baker pp. 48 (all), 51; the British Nutrition Foundation p. 85;
Trevor Clifford pp. 31, 35, 37, 43, 44, 69, 71 (bottom), 72, 91
(both), 111, 113, 119; C.M. Dixon p. 6 (top right and bottom
right); Chris Honeywell pp. 9 (middle), 109; Sylvia Macdonald,
*British Baker* p. 49; Noon Products plc pp. 16, 20 (right);
Photographers Library p. 94; Reed International Books Ltd p. 71
(top); Reed International Books Ltd/Bryce Attwell p. 67; Reed
International Books Ltd/Martin Brigdale p. 71 (2nd top); Reed
International Books Ltd/Laurie Evans p. 71 (2nd bottom), 68
(both); Reed International Books Ltd/James Jackson p. 66; Reed
International Books Ltd/James Merrell p. 47 (right); Reed
International Books Ltd/Ian O'Leary p. 47 (left); Safeway Stores
plc p. 9 (bottom right); J. Sainsbury plc pp. 23 (both), 26 (both),
27; Meg Sullivan pp. 18, 19 (all), 20 (left and middle); Tesco Stores
Ltd p. 29; Werner Forman Archive p. 6 (top left and bottom left);
Zefa p. 9 (left and top right).

The publishers have made every effort to trace copyright holders.
However, if any material has been incorrectly acknowledged, we
would be pleased to correct this at the earliest opportunity.

# Contents

# What is food technology?

## Raw materials and commodities

Everyone is an expert about food from a personal point of view. It is a subject which everyone has opinions about, such as what foods they like, what foods they don't like and so on. Eating is an everyday activity. Food is a **basic human need** and is essential to life.

How do the products pictured above begin their life? What does this have to do with food technology?

Here are the connections:
▶ Food manufacture makes **edible** materials out of agricultural produce, produce from the sea and fresh water sources.
▶ There is world-wide production of plants (crops), animals and fish to supply foods to eat.
▶ These plants, animals and fish are the **raw materials** from which food is produced.
▶ Raw materials are called **commodities**. Some examples are shown in the next illustration.

■ Some commodities

Most commodities are not edible as they are and nearly all food commodities have to be treated or processed. The reasons for processing food are answers to questions that have been asked since the beginnings of human life:
How can we **prepare** and **preserve** raw materials produced on land and in the sea?
How can we **transform** these into **food products**?

## So what is food processing?

Food processing involves changing raw materials into edible products. In food technology this is called **conversion**. Conversion is done by two processes:

**Primary processing** is the conversion of raw produce into foodstuffs which can be eaten. An example of this is cleaning and trimming vegetables. Primary processing is also the conversion of raw produce into materials which can be used to make edible foodstuffs, for example, milling wheat to make flour.

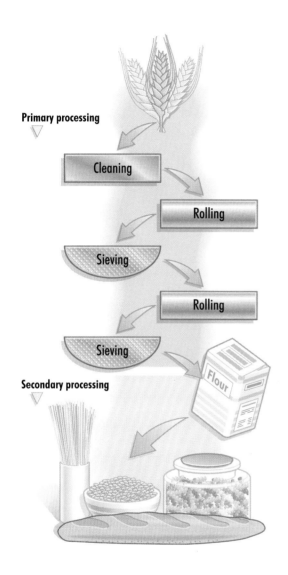

Primary processing

Cleaning

Rolling

Sieving

Rolling

Sieving

Flour

Secondary processing

In order to meet the expectations of consumers, the food industry must use the specialist skills of a wide range of people together with up-to-date machinery and production methods. The food industry is highly **mechanized** and highly **industrialized**.

The knowledge and experience of the following people are used in food product development:
▸ chemical, production and electrical engineers
▸ bacteriologists
▸ home economists
▸ food technologists
▸ market researchers
▸ nutritionists
▸ legal experts.

Working together these people must apply their knowledge of physics, chemistry, biology and nutrition science to ensure that products are of the best possible quality.

## What then is food technology?

Food technology includes all the aspects of food manufacture which have been described here. It plays a central role in:
▸ improving processing techniques
▸ improving production methods e.g. saving time, minimizing waste, extending the shelf life of products
▸ developing new products
▸ extending product ranges
▸ modifying product ranges
▸ modifying products
and many more!

Working as a food technologist involves understanding and applying knowledge of:
▸ the physical, chemical, nutritional and biological characteristics of ingredients
▸ processing techniques and the changes they can bring about
▸ those proportions, ratios, timings, sequences of actions and sensory attributes which give good reliable results.

**Secondary processing** is the conversion of the **products of primary processing** (i.e. the raw materials) into edible foodstuffs. Examples of secondary processing include flour to bread, milk to cheese and complete 'ready-to-eat' dishes.

## What part does industry play?

The food industry responds to **consumer needs** and **demands** by:
▸ producing attractive nutritious food products which are enjoyable and safe to eat
▸ constantly increasing the range and type of products available
▸ maintaining a supply of consistent and good quality products for the mass market.

# Is food technology new?

*F*ood production has always been an essential part of everyday life. Early peoples hunted, gathered and collected food to satisfy their food needs. The basic human need to eat has always driven people to:
▶ improve the food supply
▶ extend the food supply
▶ preserve food
▶ store food safely
▶ trade in food.

■ These rock carvings (here coloured white) show Bronze Age people hunting with bows and arrows, axes and spears

## Early food technology

As the photos on this page show, we have plenty of evidence of how our ancestors provided and processed food. **Archaeologists** have helped to trace the beginnings of food technology. At sites where early people lived, they have discovered tools and equipment that were used to make food palatable and safe to eat. These finds show that early people discovered three important facts about food:

**1** Water is an essential **element** for life and for food processing.

■ A replica of a 'crannog'. This type of dwelling was used by Celtic people from the Bronze Age to medieval times. It consists of buildings on a platform which is raised on stilts over water

**2** Fire is a source of **power** which can bring about changes in food.

■ A sculpture from ancient Greece showing a woman fanning a fire used for cooking

**3 Grinding**, **pounding** and **mixing** techniques make food more palatable.

■ A hand mill dating from the Neolithic period, used for grinding corn

These three discoveries form the foundation of modern food technology and they are used in the two basic processes involved in food processing.

## The two basic processes in food processing

The two processes are:
▶ the application and withdrawal of heat
▶ mixing ingredients.

These processes are used to convert raw materials into edible products in both domestic and commercial processing.

Over recent years, a significant change is taking place in our eating habits. There is a shift away from 'home cooking' towards convenience, ready-made, 'cook-in' and 'take-away' foods.

The food industry has been quick to respond to this, using all the technology available. Even during a time of high unemployment, pre-prepared and ready-made foods have continued to be popular.

The development of food technology has led to the supply of a wide and constantly increasing variety of safe, fresh and processed foods, at prices which the consumer is prepared to pay and in forms which fit in with modern lifestyles.

## Has food technology changed society?

To a large extent, food technology has changed society. For example, domestic preparation and provision of food has been made easier and quicker; the availability of pre-prepared food means that every family member can now prepare meals.

Other examples of changes that have probably occurred as a result of the developments in food technology are:

▶ It is more profitable for a family member to earn money outside the home than stay at home preparing and cooking food.
▶ Countries, societies and regions where people can leave the production of food to someone else have developed faster.
▶ Changes in employment opportunities have occurred due to the development of the food industry and the machinery, chemicals and other industries that supply it.

## Tasks

1 Look at the flow diagram which traces the changes in food technology over time. Investigate roughly when in time each change took place. You may find books about 'social history' will help to provide information for this task.

2 Here is a list of some of the modern effects on society of food technology:
 ▶ fewer family meals
 ▶ snacking
 ▶ changes in the role of women in the home
 ▶ car ownership
 ▶ availability of a wide range of food stuffs throughout the year

 a Choose one of the above changes.
  (i) Collect evidence which shows the effect the change has had where you live.
  (ii) Collate the evidence you have collected.
  (iii) Draw a conclusion which highlights the advantages and/or disadvantages of the change.
 b (i) List two or three other changes which you have noticed.
  (ii) Analyse the effects of each in terms of the opportunities they offer for the development of food products.

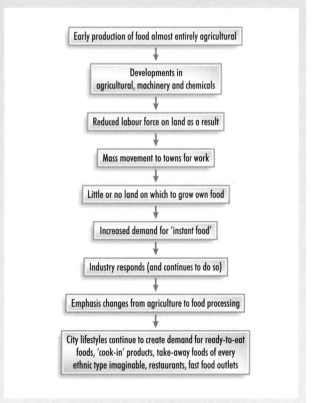

Early production of food almost entirely agricultural

↓

Developments in agricultural, machinery and chemicals

↓

Reduced labour force on land as a result

↓

Mass movement to towns for work

↓

Little or no land on which to grow own food

↓

Increased demand for 'instant food'

↓

Industry responds (and continues to do so)

↓

Emphasis changes from agriculture to food processing

↓

City lifestyles continue to create demand for ready-to-eat foods, 'cook-in' products, take-away foods of every ethnic type imaginable, restaurants, fast food outlets

■ A chronological flow diagram of stages in food production

# Food technology today

The changes referred to in the last two units have brought about rapid and varied developments in food products and in food processing methods. Consumer spending on food creates 'profitable' opportunities within the food industry. Recent figures show that:

▸ about £40 billion per year is spent on food in the UK
▸ about £1 billion is invested in the food industry every year.

## What effect does the consumer have?

Consumer demand affects the food industry in a number of ways but the demand is always towards increasing existing product ranges and producing new ones. Consumer demands arise from needs, and products are not successful unless they meet those needs.

Consumer needs fall into a number of categories such as nutritional, enjoyment and economic. New products are developed to meet one or more of these needs. These needs are known as **prompts**. A prompt will lead a company to do an initial investigation to find out if it is worth developing the idea further.

Developing new products and improving and extending product ranges is expensive, so a company needs to feel there is a good chance of succeeding and making a profit before the full product development process starts.

A prompt acts as a starting point. It can arise from some of these general areas:

▸ a gap in the market
▸ new consumer pressures
▸ a drop in consumer loyalty
▸ successful products made by competitors
▸ loss of market share
▸ new information e.g. the Government's 'Eight Guidelines for a Healthy Diet' (1995)
▸ special needs
▸ new ideas.

Developments may also be prompted by some of these more specific areas:

▸ demand for luxury items
▸ creation of particular sensory attributes e.g. texture, taste
▸ family size and life-style variations
▸ special occasions
▸ foods and dishes from a particular cultural tradition
▸ cost limitations
▸ availability of a by-product of another development.

## Tasks

1 Suggest two other specific areas which might prompt development. Add them to the list.
2 A prompt leads a manufacturer towards a particular consumer group: the 'target market' or 'target group' for the product.
   a Choose two of the more specific areas mentioned earlier.
   b Visit a supermarket and identify as many products as you can which have been developed to target each of the areas you have chosen.
   c Record your findings.
   d Choose one of the products you have identified. How successfully do you think the product meets the needs and expectations of the target market? Why do you think this is so?

## How does rapid development affect the food industry?

Food producers and manufacturers have to keep a check on their own degree of success and progress, and that of their main competitors, to keep up with technological developments and changes in consumer buying habits and expectations.

Other areas in which the industry is involved include finding the most **cost effective** ways of production and maintaining the highest standards of safety and quality in products. There are specific demands arising from these areas which the industry must meet. These include:

▸ **efficiency** of production and distribution

reduction in waste (referred to as **minimizing** waste)

extending the **shelf-life** of products

**innovation** (bringing in new methods, new ideas).

## Who is involved in food product development?

There are some manufacturers who are known particularly for certain products. These manufacturers are called **brand leaders**. Kelloggs and Heinz are two examples of this. For example, Kelloggs' cornflakes and Heinz baked beans are known to the majority of consumers and are the automatic choice of many. Certain other products become associated with a name, for example, the yeast extract, MARMITE. This name is a recognizable brand name which is legally protected so that no other company may use it. MARMITE is a registered trade mark, owned by CPC International Inc. in most countries of the world for use with yeast extract. Other manufacturers produce **own brand** or **own label** products for retailers.

## *Tasks*

3  Visit a supermarket.

   a  How many other brands of baked beans are there, apart from Heinz? Compare the weights, prices and ingredients.

   b  What other 'cornflake-type' products are there, apart from Kelloggs? Study the packaging. Are the other products easy to distinguish from the Kelloggs product? Why do you think this is so?

4  How do manufacturers and retailers try to encourage various groups of people to buy their products? Look at the photos. Give one way in which products are marketed to appeal to each of the groups shown.

# What is product development about?

The prime **aim** of food manufacturers is to produce a **consistent product** that the consumer will buy and will enjoy enough to keep on buying it. The prime **objective** of industry is to make a **profit**. However, setting up the teams of people and the machinery and other factors involved in the development of a product is expensive and if the product does not sell well, the **set-up** costs are not covered by sales and a **loss** is made, instead of a profit. Manufacturers cannot afford to make losses so they carry out a great deal of **research** before any product reaches the shelf in order to make sure that the development of that product is worthwhile and profitable.

## What does consistent mean?

A consistent product is one which is:

▶ as the consumer expects it to be – for example the taste, texture, size, weight, ingredient mix and ratio, value for money etc. must meet consumer expectations
▶ safe to eat
▶ as described and/or advertised
▶ of good quality
▶ the same as the original specification used for its development.

## The size of the market

Consumers are the people whom manufacturers are trying to attract. They are the **market**. The number of people living in the UK at any one time (the **population size**) does not vary a great deal. This means that the size of the market remains very much the same. As a result, manufacturers must compete for their share of this market. Manufacturers have to be competitive in many different ways, to try to lead the market and have the major (largest) portion of the market share.

Well-known products, as well as new products, are advertised and marketed in ways intended to persuade or remind the consumer to buy them, to swell sales. One example of a product which has been on the market for a long time is cornflakes. A well-known brand was advertised deliberately to remind the consumer, using phrases such as 'Have you forgotten how good they taste?'. Other advertisements for the same brand of cornflakes have been encouraging people to eat the product at different times of the day. In fact the advertisements suggest that there is no time nor occasion when this brand of cornflakes is not appropriate.

The Family Household Survey figures for breakfast cereal consumption show that all households spent 33.5p per person per week on breakfast cereals in 1994. The company that makes the well-known brand of cornflakes is making sure that they get a good share of that market.

## ▬ Task ▬

1  a  Visit a supermarket and identify one type of breakfast cereal other than cornflakes.
   b  Ask the manager or another employee what the volume of sales of the other cereal is compared with that of cornflakes.
   c  Is there a difference? Why do you think this is? Do the products appeal to different types of people?

Manufacturers monitor sales in this way to identify the volume of sales but also the type of person who buys the product (this is sometimes referred to as the **market profile**). The information you found out in parts **b** and **c** of this task will probably show different market profiles for the two breakfast cereals.

## Life-cycles

Every product has a life-cycle. What does this mean? To begin with it is important to understand that some products remain popular over a long period of time and require only very small adjustments from time to time in order to maintain their popularity. Examples of adjustments include updating the people who are associated with the product in advertisements to make sure they are modern and contemporary, and making small changes to the packaging.

For some products sales start very slowly and climb to a **peak** (the maximum sales achieved by this product) which is followed by a gradual drop in sales (called a **decline**). Other products have a shorter life and pass relatively quickly through the stages of growth to stages of decline – where sales can sometimes fall with alarming speed.

Falling sales can be livened up by various marketing techniques such as the introduction of new flavours or sizes and by free gifts, special offers and so on.

■ The life-cycle of a product

## Task

2 a Choose a food product which has been around for a long time. Examples include various types of chocolate bar, baked beans, salt and vinegar potato crisps.

 b Look at the appearance, consistency, texture etc. of the product. What are your opinions? Record them.

 c Taste the product. What do you think of its taste? Record your opinions.

 d What about the container, wrapping, packaging – do they tell you something about the product? Record your opinions.

 e When would you eat your chosen product? Would it be your first choice for this purpose? Record your opinions.

In this task you have 'taken a product apart' in a very simple way. Your opinions show what you think of the product. You have formed opinions about the **attributes** (the characteristics and qualities) of the product. This is called **attribute analysis** (analysis is when you have examined something to find out what it is made up of). Attribute analysis (sometimes called **disassembly**) is an important part of learning about food technology.

■ Examples of popular branded products

# 2.2 Developing food products

## How do ideas for products arise?

In Unit 1.3 there is a list of prompts which may act as starting points for the development of a product (see page 8). They are some of the common starting points for products. Sometimes brainstorming sessions give rise to exciting possibilities. This is a useful way of thinking up ideas when you are working in a **product development** team in school.

There are also other starting points. For example, one of the buyers of packaging materials for a large manufacturer saw product development possibilities while studying the characteristics of some new packaging which had been designed. This design allowed food to be sterilized within the sealed pack which contained it. The buyer saw new opportunities for developing products packed in this way. They would have a long shelf-life (about nine months) at ambient temperatures, rather than needing refrigeration or freezing. What the buyer saw was a possibility of using this packaging to produce improved **ambient ready meals**. (Ambient means safe storage is possible at room temperature, without lowering the temperature as in chilling, refrigeration and freezing.) Ambient ready meals tend to have a poor image when compared with chilled or frozen products, so the buyer's idea was thought to be worth developing further, to create a bigger market for ambient products.

This is one example of how an idea was generated. This is sometimes called **concept generation** (concepts are ideas).

## Testing new concepts

Sometimes ideas are easy to think up, but they may not be practical or realistic. Therefore they have to be tested or **screened** to see if it is worthwhile taking them further. To do this, the producer has to consider:
▸ the market opportunity
▸ the cost in relation to return, i.e. what the consumer may be willing to pay for such a product
▸ the feasibility of production i.e. is it manageable, practical and possible?

Many concepts fail at this point because however exciting they may sound, the product development team (see pages 22–30) must feel confident that the product will sell well at a price which both covers the costs of development, launching and production and makes a profit. If the concept passes the screening, development continues.

In the case of the ambient product described above, the development team felt it was worthwhile to go ahead. They decided that there was a gap in the market for a high-quality product of this type. The research which they carried out that led to this decision was focused on other ambient products which were already available. These included many dried and canned products, but the team felt that their product would have advantages over these.

Having decided to go ahead, they aimed for a high-quality ready meal made with fresh and 'healthy' ingredients (e.g. low fat), without additives, in a pack which was convenient and safe to store.

## Task

1 a Identify an ambient product of this type.
  b Describe the appearance of the food and the packaging.
  c Note the 'use-by' date.
  d Cook the product according to the pack instructions.
  e Comment upon the texture, consistency, aroma and taste of the product. Record your comments.
  f If you had been part of the development team, would you have developed this product? Why? Use your observations and comments to help you answer.

In your own work of designing and making products it is often helpful to keep a record of your opinions about existing products such as the one you chose for this task. This will allow you to use other people's ideas and expertise in your own product development tasks. You may like what they did or you may dislike some aspects of what they did and feel you can improve the product. This could become a prompt which leads you to a product concept.

## What happens next?

What happens next varies according to the company, but generally the home economists in the team begin to formulate a **recipe** for testing. To do this, they need to apply knowledge of the **functional characteristics** of food (see pages 60–71) together with new (novel, innovative) food combinations which will lead to an appetizing and nutritious product of the correct consistency and texture. The term used to describe these qualities is **organoleptic** (to do with the sensory qualities of appearance, taste, aroma and mouth feel). The home economists are given criteria to work with which could include reference to the main ingredients to use, the type of dish to aim for and so on.

At this stage the recipe is usually made on a domestic scale using small quantities to make one dish or a small batch as a development sample.

Careful and detailed notes must be taken throughout. These will include reference to:
▶ types and amounts of ingredients used (including everything that is used, even small amounts of flavouring such as herbs and spices etc.)
▶ proportion and ratio of ingredients
▶ processing methods and details (e.g. shape and size of ingredients, mixing, time, cooking method, temperature etc.)
▶ presentation and serving details including accompaniments (e.g. dips, sauces etc.).

The notes are important because if the product is 'right', this is the only information available to reproduce the product exactly.

**Sensory testing** (organoleptic analysis) is carried out on the first sample product. From this, decisions are made about the product such as:
▶ whether any modifications are necessary
▶ if so, what must be done and how
▶ whether the modifications are minor or major – are they worth doing or not?

This simple flow diagram shows these stages.

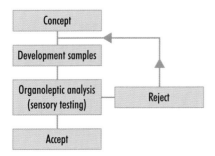

If the sample is rejected, more samples are made and tested. This continues until a satisfactory product is made. Development teams try to get it right first time because making many attempts is expensive and time-consuming.

The sensory testing at this stage is often carried out 'in house', using a team of experienced **tasters**. Tasters can be trained to analyse and comment upon organoleptic qualities. There are details about tasting on pages 98–105. This is a type of market research which gives the team some indication of reactions to their product.

## Scaling up the recipe

When the product reaches the **accept stage** the recipe formulation is scaled up in quantity, sometimes to a **prototype** scale or a **first production trial run**. This scaling up is a half-way measure between domestic (small-scale or one-off production) and commercial mass production.

The scaled-up quantities must be in exactly the same proportions as in the sample. The scaling-up calculation is often done by computer. The processing details and the critical control points (see pages 84–9) that must be included are put together with the scaled-up recipe formulation and these become the **specification** for the product at this stage. The products of the first production or trial run are tested for many things including:
▶ micro-organisms
▶ foreign bodies
▶ acidity levels
▶ weight and proportion of main or important ingredients (e.g. a dish based on chicken in a sauce must not be all sauce and hardly any chicken)
▶ sensory qualities.

At this stage consumers may be asked what their reaction to the product would be. Sometimes market research companies are asked to carry out this task, but this can be very expensive.

## Does scaling up affect the quality of a product?

Sometimes an unwanted development occurs during the trial run – for example a sauce could be too thick to go through the machinery. In this case modifications would have to be made to thin the sauce, i.e. decrease its **viscosity**, so that processing will be successful. Care would need to be taken to make sure that thinning the sauce did not alter the flavour. During the trial run checks are made to make sure that:

▶ quality control procedures are effective and clear
▶ processing techniques are appropriate and effective
▶ no part of the process takes longer than it should.

If necessary, modifications are carried out to perfect the system. This is sometimes called **product technical approval** and may lead to a factory trial. The products of the factory trial are tested further and if the results are acceptable first production takes place.

## Other parts of the development

At the same time as the product is being developed and tested, the packaging has to be designed and the consumer information must be prepared. The work-flow diagram below shows the whole process in sequence.

The stage in the work-flow labelled 'Technical approval of product' involves producing information about: the specification, the flow diagram, hazard analysis and shelf-life details.

A product can be launched onto the market in several ways, including:

▶ press launch, where journalists are invited to hear a presentation by the company about the product. (The aim here is to get some high-profile media coverage via newspapers, radio, television)
▶ trialling the product in selected regions of the country or particular types of retail outlets
▶ advertising
▶ mail shots which include free samples.

## Product life-cycles and profitability

Once the product has been launched, sales can be monitored so that evidence about the possible life-cycle and profitability can be collected. The production costs are made up of the cost of:

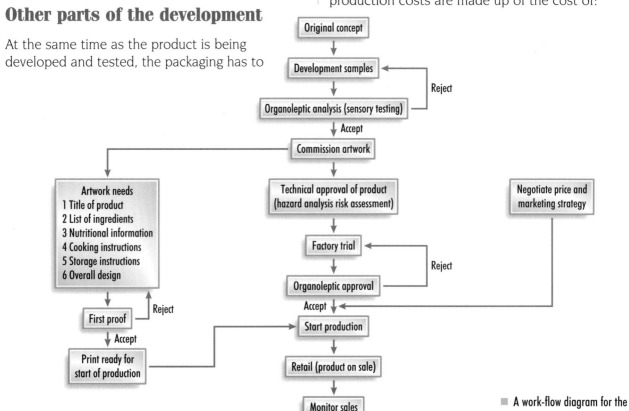

■ A work-flow diagram for the development of a product

▶ product development activities
▶ setting up the processing plant
▶ raw materials (including ingredients and packaging materials)
▶ labour and mechanical energy used to drive the process
▶ testing and advertising.

Some of these are **fixed costs** e.g. the first two in the list above, which are incurred no matter how many products are made. Other costs are dependent on the quantity of products being made and include for example raw materials, labour, energy, advertising and promotion. These are **variable costs**. Fixed costs plus variable costs make up the total cost.

Most products make a loss to begin with until the level of sales rises beyond the level at which production costs (fixed costs) are covered. This is called the **break-even** stage. Profits are made from that stage on as long as the product remains popular.

## How can this information be used in school product development work?

If you are designing and making products to specifications, costing must be part of the process. One of the important lessons to be learned in food technology is that a carefully designed product that meets consumers' needs is almost always a winner, whereas a product which is less carefully designed in terms of value to consumer is almost always a loser. The diagram below shows how this works.

> **Carry out Market Research**
> Find the attributes consumers want in a product.
> Design new product with these attributes.

> **Recognize Simple Quality Attributes of Product**
> Do not carry out more testing than necessary as consumer considers basic qualities, e.g. taste, colour, texture.

> **Find economic price range for product**
> Consumers will not pay more than they think the product is worth.

■ Planning appropriate quality levels for a food product

## Quality of design and cost

The quality of design must meet consumer expectation e.g. is the product a standard, economy or premium line? If the product is an economy line, for example an own-brand staple food such as flour, the quality of design must be as high as possible within the low-cost limitations for such a product. The consumers will stop buying the product if the quality does not meet their expectations. Even in a low-cost economy line consumers expect a high-quality product but without frills. There is a limit to the amount consumers will pay for quality beyond the level considered to be the best (called the **optimum** level). This is particularly important to remember when developing premium products (i.e. those with a luxury or expensive image). Although consumers may be willing to pay more for such a product, there is a limit to *how much more* will be seen as a reasonable amount. Therefore, if a product is made to a level of quality beyond the optimum the extra production costs involved will be wasted because there will be no added value to the consumer.

### ═ *Task* ═

2 a Select two or three products from the store cupboard at school or at home. Make sure one of them is a premium product.

b Find out the price of each product. What do you get for the money? Study the contents and assess their quality, for example if you have chosen a jar of jam, look at the amount and size of the fruit.

c Do the products seem to be good value? Is the price reasonable for the type of product? Is the optimum level of quality reached?

## Where can commercial food-processing methods be seen?

Factory visits and videos showing manufacturing techniques are very helpful. Sometimes, however, a visit cannot be arranged and there isn't a suitable video available. Unit 2.3 is a case study of a visit to a factory and traces a cook-chill product from development through to production.

## Product development at Noon Products plc

Noon Products plc specializes in the production of chilled and frozen Indian ready meals.

1 The basis of all Noon Products is authentic Indian cooking, backed up by technology. Product development starts with ideas from traditional domestic recipes which are scaled up to commercial quantities if they meet all the criteria set down for development.
2 Most products are based on chicken, a sauce and rice.
3 The business has a 'family' image, not a **corporate** one (i.e. it is not a big company). Emphasis is placed on the fact that every employee has a personal responsibility to ensure the quality of a product. This makes for a very tight-knit organization.
4 Only the best and freshest raw materials are used. The company directors source and buy all the raw materials to match the company's speciality requirements. This allows the company to have total control over the quality of the products they produce. For example, about 30 tonnes of graded chicken fillets are bought each week, and prepared 'in house'. This gives the company total control over the quality of chicken used.

Vegetables are bought in the UK when in season, otherwise they come from wherever offers the best quality, e.g. Holland, France, Spain. They are also prepared in house. Speciality raw materials come from all over the world e.g. ginger and garlic from China, green chillies and spices etc. from wherever the best quality is offered.

5 Additives are not used. Some of the raw materials used in Indian cookery, e.g. the spices, give the dishes a natural shelf-life because they have a preservative effect, which means that additives which are normally used to preserve foods are not required. In addition to this, domestic methods of processing are used at Noon so that, for example, sauces are thickened by evaporating some of the liquid off in the same way as a sauce would be prepared in the home. The people at Noon

■ Welcome to Noon Products plc

believe that if a thickener is not needed at home, then it is not needed in manufacture.

6 It is relatively easy to produce a good product if the processing is kept simple; however, the more stages there are in the processing, the more difficult it is to achieve a good product.

7 Noon produces six products under its own label as well as a large proportion of the 'Indian lines' of ready meals sold by three major retailers.

8 The company first established itself in the UK but now exports to Europe, too.

## Quality and production

There has been a steady increase in demand for highly-spiced and Indian-type ready meal dishes. This is mainly as a result of the number of restaurants serving curried and spicy foods which have opened in the last 20 years. Consumers want to be able to eat this type of food at home as well and thus demand has created a market.

   This is the success story of a market opportunity which has been made the most of by a company. Its continuing success is due to the company's insistence on high quality throughout production. How is this done?

▶ Every employee must take responsibility for carrying out their tasks to the quality which meets the specification for those tasks. Employees must 'sign off' a task when it has been completed to their satisfaction.

▶ Critical control points (see pages 80–9) are checked and monitored by a team of quality controllers at regular intervals throughout the day.

▶ The company has its own microbiological laboratory. The qualified staff test raw materials, products at various stages during processing and also finished products. The laboratory also carries out regular checks on the hygiene of the factory environment and of the personnel.

▶ Chefs are trained by the company for at least two years before they are given the opportunity to be innovative in recipe development and given independent responsibility.

Examples of Noon brand products include:
▶ Traditional Chicken Curry and Pilau Rice (net weight: 340 grams)

▶ Chicken Tikka in Pasanda Sauce and Pilau Rice (net weight: 340 grams)
▶ Chicken Tikka Makhanwala and Pilau Rice (net weight: 340 grams)
▶ Traditional Prawn Curry and Pilau Rice (net weight: 340 grams)
▶ Lamb Roganjosh and Pilau Rice (net weight: 400 grams)
▶ Vegetable Jalfrezi and Masala Dal (net weight: 400 grams).

Another indication of quality is the ratio of the ingredients. For example, a dish with a large amount of rice and a very small amount of chicken would not meet the quality standard set by this company. This is how the net weights of the above dishes are made up:

| All Chicken Curry products: | Rice 140 grams<br>Chicken 70 grams<br>Sauce 130 grams |
| --- | --- |
| Prawn Curry and Pilau Rice: | Rice 140 grams<br>Prawns 55 grams<br>Sauce 145 grams |
| Lamb Roganjosh and Pilau Rice: | Rice 140 grams<br>Lamb 60 grams<br>Sauce 140 grams |
| Vegetable Jalfrezi and Marsala Dal: | Vegetable Jalfrezi 200 grams<br>Marsala Dal 200 grams. |

   Another example is where an expensive ingredient (called a **premium ingredient**) such as cashew nuts is used. The amount used in the recipe formulation must be sufficient to give the dish a characteristic cashew nut quality (e.g. through flavour, use of whole nut etc.) without being so expensive as to take the production cost beyond its retail price range. In the production of a cook-chill ready meal of Chicken and Cashew Nuts with Egg Fried Rice, the cashew nuts are counted as they are added to each dish to exactly the number in the specification for the product. If too few nuts are added the product will not meet the specification, if too many are added the product becomes too expensive and is also outside the specification.

   A product flow process diagram for a typical cook-chill product, including temperatures etc. is shown on the following page.

**Product flow**

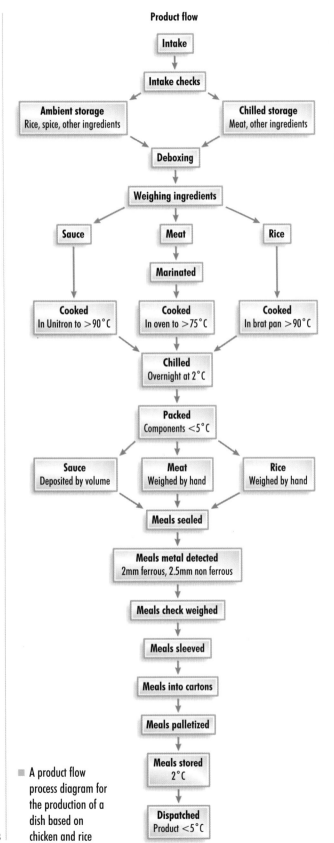

```
Intake
  ↓
Intake checks
  ↓
Ambient storage              Chilled storage
Rice, spice, other           Meat, other ingredients
ingredients
  ↓                             ↓
        Deboxing
          ↓
   Weighing ingredients
      ↓    ↓    ↓
  Sauce   Meat   Rice
           ↓
        Marinated
  ↓        ↓        ↓
Cooked    Cooked    Cooked
In Unitron  In oven to   In brat pan
to >90°C    >75°C        >90°C
           ↓
        Chilled
     Overnight at 2°C
          ↓
        Packed
    Components <5°C
  ↓        ↓        ↓
Sauce    Meat      Rice
Deposited  Weighed   Weighed
by volume  by hand   by hand
        Meals sealed
          ↓
   Meals metal detected
2mm ferrous, 2.5mm non ferrous
          ↓
   Meals check weighed
          ↓
    Meals sleeved
          ↓
   Meals into cartons
          ↓
   Meals palletized
          ↓
    Meals stored
        2°C
          ↓
     Dispatched
   Product <5°C
```

■ A product flow process diagram for the production of a dish based on chicken and rice

■ The clothing store. Mohammed Rahmatulla is showing the clothing required for the high risk and low risk areas

For the low risk area: jackets with *blue* pockets, black boots

For the high risk area: jackets with *red* pockets, white boots

Blue hairnets and hats to be worn in all areas. Blue disposable gloves. Blue is chosen for these items because, as no food is coloured blue, if these items were to fall into the food accidentally during processing they would be seen immediately

# Low risk area

■ The spices are checked for quality and then weighed according to the specification. The specification sheet is to the left of the weighing machine. The person whose responsibility it is to weigh the spices must sign the specification sheet, thus taking responsibility for checking and weighing accurately. The signature allows faults to be traced should they occur

# Low risk area

■ Spices weighed and ready to be used by the cooks. Notice the specification sheet which must remain with that batch of spices, again to enable faults to be traced should they occur

■ Diced raw chicken, coated in sauce, being placed on the wire conveyor belt which will take the chicken through the oven to be cooked. The temperature and time required are programmed into the system. The controls for one of the ovens can be seen at the top of the photo

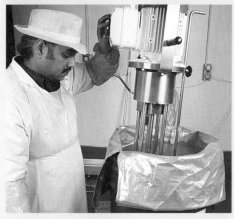

■ A large liquidizer used to reduce tomatoes and juice to a pulp

■ Pilau rice being cooked

# High risk area

Cooked chicken and rice being weighed according to the specification and put into trays

Sauce is added – deposited by machine. This means the machine has been calibrated (i.e. programmed) to deposit the required amount of sauce

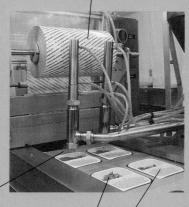

This roll is the covering film. The film is placed over two trays and cut by a machine. The trays are then moved along by a belt and the edges of the film are sealed

Weighed chicken and rice in trays

The sealed trays move along on a conveyor belt and pass through a metal detector. Each tray is also weighed to make sure the weight is within the specification. If metal is detected or the weight does not meet the specification that tray is automatically pushed into one of the two areas shown at the bottom of the picture. Both of these areas have a lock on them to prevent the rejected trays being put back into the system

# Low risk area

■ In the packing room the trays are placed in a sleeve which is stamped with a 'use by' date

■ The sleeved products are delivered to the retailer, in this case Sainsbury's, in a recyclable box. Sainsbury's do not use cardboard boxes, preferring to use these green crates for delivery and then returning them to Noon who wash and clean them ready to use again

■ Lorries arrive to be loaded with meals for J. Sainsbury and Waitrose and with Noon Products' own brands

## Using a commercial approach to help design-and-make tasks in school

The two main aspects of Noon products which can be applied are:

▶ the use of domestic and traditional recipe ideas
▶ the quality control features which form the basis of quality assurance (each operator must take responsibility for the quality of their work). At Noon, quality control procedures ensure that:

- storage, cooking and cooling temperatures are appropriate for the safety of the product at every stage during processing
- all ingredients are weighed accurately, ratios checked and the correct amounts of sauce added (called deposited or **dumped** in industry) to the product

- sealing and foreign body (e.g. metal) detection is carried out effectively
- meals are the correct weight and sleeved correctly.

Together, these control procedures provide the evidence that safe and consistent products are being made. This is called **product assurance**.

**Note:** The microbiological tests which are carried out in the factory *must not* be done in school. Controlling the environment in which dishes are cooled, packed and stored is important, however, and *can* be carried out in school. Knowledge of the temperatures which kill bacteria and of the temperatures and other conditions such as pH and moisture level which make it impossible for bacteria to grow and multiply must be applied and should form part of your specification for production (see Unit 3.5).

## — Tasks

1 In a group of four, carry out the following design-and-make task.

Design and make a product based on a traditional recipe from a culture which is different from your own.

2 The product must:
  ▶ be a cook-chill type of product
  ▶ not cost more to produce than a similar commercially produced cook-chill product costs to buy

  ▶ be capable of being scaled-up for mass production whilst maintaining the traditional effect and appeal
  ▶ have a an ingredients list, b nutrition information, c cooking instructions for oven baking and reheating in a microwave, d product description and title, e serving size information, f weight.

3 You must research:
  ▸ different cultures and traditional recipes
  ▸ commercial cook-chill products (including costs)
  ▸ nutritional composition of appropriate foods
  ▸ your own ideas to see if they are practical and feasible
  ▸ temperatures and times which are critical in the processing of cook-chill dishes in order to make sure they are safe to eat.

4 a Divide the work up among the members of the team, for example:
  ▸ one person researches cultures and traditional recipes
  ▸ one person researches commercial cook-chill products
  ▸ one person researches the hazards which can occur when making cook-chill products
  ▸ one person identifies the tools, equipment, resources and appropriate raw materials which are available.

  b Get together to discuss the results of the research (some of which could be a homework task!).

5 Use the information you have gained from your research to help you to generate ideas for products which fit the requirements listed in 2 above.

6 ▸ Brainstorm ideas for a name and product description.
  ▸ Select the most promising.
  ▸ Produce a detailed specification which includes:
    • the recipe formulation
    • the processing stages in the order in which they must take place
    • details of the critical control points which will make sure a quality product is made. (Remember to give specific temperatures and times for carrying out a process)
    • a list of the tools, equipment and other resources which will be required
    • nutrition and other consumer information e.g. cooking instructions, serving size and weight.

7 Divide up the tasks involved in making your product among the members of the team, for example:
  ▸ one pair shares the actual production
  ▸ one pair shares the compilation (putting together) of the consumer information. (Use a computer program to help if there is one available.)

8 What do you think of the product you have made? Discuss this and make notes under either or both of the following headings.
  a The product met the specification because ...
  b The product did not meet the specification because ...

9 a Carry out a difference test. Do this by:
    ▸ asking about six people to form a tasting panel
    ▸ giving each person an unidentified sample of your product and an unidentified sample of a similar commercial product. (Remember to keep all the aspects of this situation the same i.e. same size of sample, same type and colour of plate on which the samples are given)
    ▸ identifying each sample with a code e.g. your product could be X; the commercial product Z
    ▸ asking each taster to say which product they prefer and why. (Tasters may need some help in saying why, so ask them questions such as, 'Which has the flavour you prefer?', 'Which is the most moist?' etc.)
  b Record the responses.
  c Analyse the responses. Record your conclusions. The responses may contain opinions which mean you have to modify your product if you wish to continue to develop it. They will also help you to complete your development work by drawing conclusions about whether your cook-chill product compares well with the commercial example you used.

# 2.4 The product development team

*I*t takes time, energy, effort and the expertise of several people to develop a new food product. A consumer who takes a product off the shelf to buy it has little idea of how long it has taken to develop that product. The time taken between the first idea for a product and its manufacture is called the **lead-in time**. Most products have a lead-in time of from four to six months. So who is involved in the process? The following descriptions apply to a typical product development team that may be used by any large retailing company.

## Product development manager

The product development manager is a key person who acts as a link between the members of the development team. He or she is at the centre of the development of a product and is responsible for identifying the suppliers for a particular product and for finding the best source of ingredients and materials. This is done by looking at a number of suppliers of the type of materials or foods required.

The product development manager will have discussions with a number of suppliers and will aim to find out about:
▶ their strengths and weaknesses e.g. whether they can meet the requirements
▶ whether the time scale allowed can be kept
▶ whether their machinery or plant equipment is up to the job
▶ whether the type and quality of product required can be maintained.

These are the essential pieces of information which the manager uses to decide who the supplier will be. The critical factor on which a decision rests is who will give the best quality at a particular price. Before the decision is made there may be a number of sampling sessions carried out to check quality, efficiency and so on.

After the decision is made, the supplier is given a specification which lists every detail of the requirements. In the case of the product development manager of a large supermarket chain who is looking for a supplier of an own-brand product, the specification will include a recipe. The supplier will submit a number of samples of the product and will make modifications as and if needed.

## The buyer

The buyer takes over from the manager when it is decided to everyone's satisfaction that the supplier can produce what is required, at the quality and price specified. The buyer then has responsibility for maintaining the volume and quality of supplies. This involves on-going negotiation with the supplier.

## The food technologist/technical manager

The food technologist is responsible for making sure that the functional properties and the choice and ratio of ingredients used will ensure the qualities required and meet the specification for the product. In a factory the food technologist is often the technical manager and has responsibility for making sure that production methods are hygienic, appropriate, safe, economical and efficient.

## The home economics manager/product evaluation officer

The home economics manager (sometimes called the **product evaluation officer**) is the team's food expert. The manager has a team of people who are experts in food processing and recipe formulation. The main task for this team is to formulate a recipe for a product, make up the product and test it for consistency, taste and other aspects of the specification. The aim is to establish what the product ought to taste like and what it should look like. This is so that unplanned (and unwanted) changes that can take place during processing will be prevented. The home economics team amend and modify the recipe and processing method until they are satisfied with the result. In this way, a reference point is developed which shows what the product must taste like and what it must look like. Other tasks which this team carries out include sensory testing of products.

A home economics manager's kitchen

## Task

1 a Select an own-brand commercial product.
  b Assess the appearance, texture and taste of the product.
  c Use the information you gain from b to write a reference point which could have been used by the home economics team to describe what the product must taste and look like.

A home economics team carrying out sensory testing

## Case study of a home economics department of a large retailing company

This department is part of the trading division of the company. The work the department carries out makes it an 'important attribute' to the business and merits a big investment. Product development, quality assurance and sensory testing are three important aspects of the work. The team is made up of a manager and a number of home economists. The accommodation includes a development and testing kitchen, sensory evaluation booths, a discussion room and quality control kitchens.

## Product development work

The department's work in product development is two-fold.

1 **Recipe development** e.g. for advertisements, for consumer information, on-pack recipe ideas and so on. This work includes recipe formulation and product processing. The development team produces dishes in traditional, domestic quantities and presents them attractively. The dishes are often photographed and appear on leaflets and packs with the recipe and method details so that the consumers are tempted to buy the ingredients and make the dish.

2 **Recipe development which helps to promote** a particular ingredient or raw material which the buyer would like to become more popular with the consumer. A recent example of this type of recipe development came from the buyer of offal products. These are not universally popular and the company's buyer wished to promote them. He gave the home economics department a brief which involved them in thinking up attractive and innovative recipe ideas based on different types of offal. The team categorized offal into types and produced a range of dishes for each type. Liver was one of the categories.

*How did the team approach the task?*

▶ First, they identified three different types of liver: calves, lambs' and pigs' liver.
▶ They researched the ways in which these were

■ A promotional leaflet for Thai grilled chicken

sold and, if sold in packs, how much there was in each pack (including how many servings).

▷ They then brainstormed cooking and serving methods which are popular using other meat-based dishes.

▷ They aimed to produce dishes which did not have a traditional feel, for example liver and bacon is very traditional.

▷ They identified the characteristics of liver which some consumers find off-putting, for example its texture or flavour.

### How did this approach help them to formulate ideas?

▷ They decided that marinating or soaking the liver and then adding other ingredients such as fruit and spices would encourage people to re-think their attitude to liver.

▷ They marinated some of the pigs' liver in garlic, oil and seasoning, to avoid any bitter flavour.

▷ They soaked the lambs' liver in milk to achieve the same result.

▷ They prepared the liver in a number of different ways, including cutting it into strips, and putting a tasty stuffing inside rolls of sliced liver.

### What ideas did they develop?

▷ From the calves' liver they made calves' liver olives stuffed with a forcemeat containing onion, breadcrumbs, lemon and herbs, served with a well-flavoured sauce and batons of vegetables.

▷ From the lambs' liver they made lambs' liver stir fry, where the liver was cut into strips and stir fried with strips of vegetables (e.g. red and yellow peppers) and flavoured with a 'Chinese' style sauce with a lovely sweet and sour flavour.

▷ From the pigs' liver they made a Mexican-type dish (identified by the team as being a very popular cuisine with younger people). The liver was minced and mixed with flavourings including chilli and when cooked it was served in a taco shell, accompanied by a tomato and chilli salsa.

### The result

The buyer was delighted with the dishes. These will now be developed and published as in-store recipe leaflets to promote sales.

■ These dishes are examples of a similar exercise, this time to encourage sales of tomatoes and vegetables from Jersey. The dishes also give attractive ideas for using mozzarella cheese

### JERSEY LEEK, POTATO AND MOZZARELLA TART
~ SERVES 6 ~

| | |
|---|---|
| 450g (1lb) young Jersey leeks, well washed<br>1 small sprig of thyme | Cut leeks into 1cm (½in) rings, then boil in water to cover, with the thyme, until soft, about 15 minutes. Drain well, reserving the liquor. Discard the thyme. |
| Salt and freshly ground pepper<br>8 basil leaves, cut into fine strips | Season the leeks with salt, pepper and basil. |
| 225g (8oz) Jersey Royal new potatoes, peeled and cut into 6mm (¼in) slices | Cook in the leek liquor until just soft, about 4-5 minutes. Drain, and allow to cool. |
| 200g (7oz) filo pastry, rolled out thinly | Divide into four 30cm (12in) rounds. Place three pieces of pastry rounds on top of each other in a baking tin and arrange with alternate layers of potato and leek on top. |
| 50g (2oz) butter, gently melted with a sprig of thyme | Brush each layer and trickle over the top. |
| 175g (6oz) Mozzarella cheese, diced<br>1 cooking apple, peeled, cored, diced and tossed in lemon juice<br>Salt and freshly ground pepper | Sprinkle over, and season. Top with the remaining sheet of filo and seal edges, using a little water. Prick several times with a fork and bake in the oven (moderate 160°C/325°F/Gas 3) for about 20-30 minutes. If top starts to brown too quickly, reduce the heat or cover loosely with foil. Serve warm or cold. |

### TOMATO, MOZZARELLA AND BASIL TERRINE
~ SERVES 4 ~

| | |
|---|---|
| 12-14 large ripe Jersey tomatoes | Cut to fit a small, deep terrine dish. Hold a tomato upright, stem uppermost, and cut down thick slices off the four sides, leaving a square core in the middle (discard this). This will give you four roughly rectangular 1.5cm (½in) thick slices. Cut all the tomatoes similarly. Flatten the slices gently under the palm of your hand and trim into neat rectangles. |
| 500g (18oz) Mozzarella cheese | Cut into similar slices, and trim into neat rectangles. |
| A large bunch of fresh basil | Wash, gently pat dry, and pick off the leaves. Line the terrine with cling film. Place a layer of slices of tomato, skin side-down, into the base of the terrine. Try to make the slices fit exactly to give a neat final effect. |
| Salt and freshly ground pepper | Season well and add a layer of Mozzarella slices, followed by a layer of basil leaves. Keep adding layers in the same order, finishing with a layer of tomato. Cover with cling film and a flat piece of card cut to fit the top of the terrine exactly. Place a light weight on top and chill for several hours. This will help the layers stick together. To serve, unmould carefully onto a chopping board, and slice into thick individual slices. |
| 4 sprigs fresh basil<br>Good olive oil and balsamic vinegar | Use to garnish each plate, if required. |

15

## Quality assurance

Another aspect of the home economics department's work is making sure that products are of good quality. This is called **quality assurance** and is an on-going checking procedure. The quality of existing products is checked to ensure they are within the specification. Part of this procedure involves using the products made by competitors (e.g. the brand leaders) as **bench marks** and matching the in-house product with that of the competitor for price, percentage of meat in a meat product and so on. Other quality assurance checks are carried out on a regular basis on all products. Samples of a product are drawn at random from the distribution centres by buyers of that product. Fresh trout can be used as an example. Suppose the buyer wishes to check the quality of trout from a number of suppliers. First the appearance of the raw fish is checked by the buyer, then samples of the raw trout are cooked by a member of the home economics team so that the buyer can judge the **eating quality**. This type of quality check is carried out on many products each day.

### Informing the consumer

Other work includes checking and producing information for the consumer, to minimize as far as possible any risks associated with a product. This type of check is referred to as **due diligence**. The sort of tasks involved include:
▶ extensive testing of the use of products
▶ using the methods and approach taken by the average consumer (who does not always have the knowledge nor the time available to avoid risks and hazards).

One very important aspect of this work is checking that the information given about preparing and cooking a product is accurate. For example, microwave instructions for heating a product made with meat and vegetables in a sauce must ensure that each ingredient is heated to the temperature which makes the product safe to eat.

The testing is done by heating such a product in a microwave oven in the test kitchen. Each component of the dish has a colour-coded optic fibre inserted into it which registers the internal

■ Optic fibres are inserted into the food

■ Internal temperatures are recorded by the computer system

temperature. This is monitored via a simple software package on a computer. The microwave oven is attached to a computer system, which prints out on a screen (in graph form) the internal temperature of each of the components of the dish. When the appropriate temperature levels are reached the graph freezes into a still form which can then be printed. The photos above show this procedure in operation.

## Sensory testing

Another important function of this department is sensory testing. Carrying out this type of test in house is a cost effective way of finding out how the consumer will react. This type of market research covers aspects such as:
▶ quality of new products
▶ whether old products are still what the consumer wants

▶ specific qualities (attributes) of products, such as mouth-feel attributes including moist, greasy, burning, cooling etc.

### How is the testing carried out?

To provide a good statistical base, a tasting panel of between 40 and 50 people is needed. The tasting takes place in booths. The samples are identified using a code and the tasters must record their opinions about taste, texture or any other specific characteristic. The booths are lit by different colours so that the colour of the samples does not affect the tasters' opinion. The photo below show the booths and the different colours of light.

In Unit 4 there is detailed information about sensory tasting, and how this should be organized in design-and-make activities in school (see pages 98–105).

Another example of a tasting activity is when very specific information is required, such as how to extend the shelf-life of a product. For this a much smaller team of tasters is used and these people are usually trained tasters. Training involves being able to identify and describe the appearance, odour and taste of food very precisely. These tasters have had training to develop their **palate** (their sense of taste). The training can be carried out by the home economics team which has an odour library that helps people to develop their sense of taste. This kind of tasting activity involves in-depth discussion so that appropriate decisions can be made as a result of the evidence gained from the tasting panel.

| | |
|---|---|
| Biscuity | a pleasant characteristic often found in Keemun tea. |
| Body | the strength of the liquor combined with the weight on the tongue. 'Full bodied' is the opposite of 'thin'. |
| Bright | the colour of tea when brewed should look bright to the eye. |
| Brisk | lively and sparkling – not flat |
| Character | an attractive taste derived from quality tea. |
| Coloury | depth of colour and strength. |
| Flavour | aromatic quality resulting from the slow growth of teas at a high elevation. |
| Light | lacking strength and depth of colour. |
| Malty | a subtle and underlying flavour often associated with Assam tea. |
| Strength | body or substance. |
| Thin | lacking body and/or colour. |
| Vintage | refers to quality and not age, as with wines. This is a tea of very good quality, suitable for the connoisseur. |
| Weak | refers to the amount of tea or coffee used in proportion to the amount of water. For example, if one teaspoon per pot is used when brewing tea, rather than one per person – the tea will taste weak. |

■ Tea odour library

| | |
|---|---|
| Acidity | sharp and pleasing taste that is neither sweet nor sour. Akin to the dryness of a dry white wine. |
| Body | the strength of the liquor combined with the weight on the tongue. 'Full bodied' is the opposite of 'thin'. |
| Character | an attractive taste derived from good quality coffee. |
| Cheesy | a gamey coffee with a hint of gorgonzola. |
| Earthy | a powerful characteristic of Indonesian coffee, caused by the volcanic soil. |
| Fruity | a winey, grapey, blackcurrant flavour. |
| Mild | where no particular feature is dominant – all are in perfect harmony. |
| Strength | body or substance. |
| Weak | refers to the amount of coffee used in proportion to the amount of water. Does not refer to the quality of the coffee. merely the brewing method. |

■ Coffee odour library

## Task

Begin to train your palate. This is a very simple introductory test.

2 a Work in pairs to carry out a blind tasting.

  b Prepare three different samples for your partner to taste. Put the samples in identical plastic cups. Examples could include:
  ▶ plain water
  ▶ a fruit juice (for example lemon juice)
  ▶ cold tea

  c Record your partner's opinions.

  d Change over. Repeat b and c using different samples.

It is important that the taster does not know what the samples are.

■ The booths used for sensory testing

# Product safety manager

The product safety manager plays a very important part in developing new products and also in checking existing ones. This manager is often a **microbiologist** whose main aim is to make sure products are safe to eat. In the food industry it is recognized that there are risks with everything from the supply of raw materials through to the consumer storing products in the home. The product safety manager's primary task is to reduce all risks to the very lowest level possible. The background against which this manager works is that there is inherent risk with everything and it is impossible to eliminate it completely. Product safety managers have three key areas of responsibility.

### 1 Approvals

The approvals process involves making sure that a product is safe before it appears on the shelf. It includes carrying out tests before a product is approved. These cover:
▶ raw materials
▶ process flow during processing and production – very detailed investigations and checks of times are made for a particular process, the temperatures achieved and so on
▶ holding times, including detailed investigations and checks carried out to make sure the times taken (for example for cooling products and holding products at chill temperatures) will not put the safety of products at risk
▶ shelf-life analysis – testing a product throughout the storage time claimed for that product to make sure it is safe to eat.

### 2 Surveillance

One aspect of surveillance is the continuous monitoring of products at the **point of sale** (where they are sold) to make sure that they comply with the specification.

Observation and checking techniques ensure that products remain safe and are of good quality throughout their life-cycle. The way surveillance is carried out varies between manufacturers. Some use outside consultants for this work and some carry it out themselves, in house. Whichever way is used the responsibility is with the product safety manager.

Microbiological tests are also carried out on products on a regular basis. The products are bought exactly as a consumer buys them; they are not produced specifically for testing. They are taken off the shelf, bought and then analysed for micro-organisms. This is an essential aspect of the controls which manufacturers carry out to assure consumers that their products are safe. This continuous survey provides confirmation that all the safety and quality systems in the production chain are working efficiently.

### 3 Emerging issues survey

This area of responsibility involves the product safety manager being constantly informed about developments which could affect product safety so that consumers are not exposed to new risks. For example, a recent concern about consumer understanding of the correct cooking of a thick burger product involved the product safety manager of a supermarket chain carrying out tests to establish correct times, temperatures and distance from the heat source so that new cooking instructions could be put on the packaging of these burgers. This made sure they would be safe to eat when consumers grilled them.

# Laboratory accreditation co-ordinator

Another member of some product safety teams for whom the manager has responsibility is the laboratory accreditation co-ordinator. A vital part in making sure that products are safe and of good quality is the testing, much of which is carried out in a laboratory. The laboratory provides information and results which confirm – or otherwise – whether a product meets the specification. This is a very important aspect of any quality system.

Laboratories can be in house or the work can be given to an outside laboratory which specializes in this work. The laboratory work is tested against a quality standard (based on European standard EN45001, which states the general criteria for the operation of testing laboratories).

The co-ordinator is responsible to the supplier and/or the manufacturer and must make sure these standards are met by the laboratory.

■ Food testing in a laboratory

## The legal expert

The product development team also includes a legal expert. The legal expert is not usually consulted during the early stages of development but is responsible for making sure everything being considered for development is legal. This includes ensuring that:

▶ the product name is clear, not misleading and not a copy (or close to a copy) of another product made by anybody else

▶ any claim attached to the product is correct and meets any legislation which exists, such as a nutrition labelling directive or guidelines for the control of nutrition claims (see pages 34–5)

▶ the product is sufficiently different from one made by a competitor.

The legal expert normally signs the final design briefs to show that these three aspects have been cleared. The legal aspects are increasingly important for two main reasons.

▶ There is legislation which covers many aspects of development, including product names, recipe formulation (ingredient combinations), additives and so on.

▶ Manufacturers are protective of their own products and do not want their best ideas to be used by a competitor. For example, recently a new fizzy drink was developed that was very like a famous cola. There was a great deal of legal discussion about whether it was too similar to the famous product. If a new product is too similar to an already-famous product with which the name of that type of product is associated (the cola referred to earlier is an example), it could mean

that the consumer would buy it thinking it was the famous product. When the name of a product becomes the one associated with that type of product, that name is often used for all products of the same type. The term 'hoover' for vacuum cleaners is an example of this. This name becomes the generic name for that type of product.

*What other responsibilities does the legal expert have?*

The development of food products is regulated in many ways. For example, there is legislation which controls:

▶ the additives that may be used, and the amount which may be used (referred to as the level)

▶ any nutritional claims made about the product

▶ any medicinal claims made for the product. (In fact medicinal claims cannot be made without a licence.)

The legal expert also checks any advertising to make sure it is not misleading and that it is legally correct. One example is the use of **barker cards** in retail outlets. These are large cards placed throughout a store which advertise special offers such as 'three for the price of two', etc.

In addition many legal experts who work with food companies **lobby** (try to influence) the European Union (EU) about products which are common in the UK but may not be seen in other parts of the EU. They also have the responsibility of answering questions raised about the name of a product, the additives used, the types and ratios of ingredients and so on.

## ▬ *Task* ▬

3 a Carry out an investigation to discover how close to another manufacturer's product a competitor's product is. Choose one type of product on which to base your investigation (cola is a good example).

  b Study the colours used on the packaging or container – including the number and the combinations. Compare them for similarity. Study the names and words which appear on the product. Look at the typeface and the height and width of the letters.

  c Write a conclusion. Give examples to support your conclusion.

# The company nutritionist

The company nutritionist usually has a team of people to formulate and carry out a nutritional strategy which is used in product development. This involves applying current dietary guidelines and understanding how the consumer can be guided to make food choices which support those guidelines. Other aspects include making decisions about increasing the nutritive value of certain products by nutritional enhancement and nutritional fortification. The company nutritionist must know about the special needs of particular groups of people, when making these decisions, as well as considering the following points.

▶ Is the enhancement or fortification justified?
▶ Can the production process carry it out effectively and efficiently? (Put another way, is it industrially viable? This is a question usually asked to make sure that the process will not be too expensive.)
▶ What type of product is to be enhanced or fortified? This needs to be considered because, for example, if the product is a standard product, such as bread, for which the consumer is used to paying a particular price, any extra cost as a result of increasing the nutritive value may mean the product will not sell. If, however, the product is a premium product (one for which the consumer is willing to pay a little more because it has a luxury image) the extra cost will not deter the consumer in quite the same way.
▶ How will the nutritive value be increased? It is important to make sure no group of consumers is disadvantaged by the fortification.

The nutritionists work with the whole product development team to provide the choice of products which consumers expect.

# What other responsibilities do the nutritionists have?

Consumers do not respond well to **nutrition messages**, they understand food messages more readily and find them easier to understand. Company nutritionists interpret government recommendations and produce **consumer-friendly** information and advice. There has been misunderstanding and confusion about the types and amounts of foods which should be eaten and as a result many company nutritionists have been given the responsibility of producing information which people can understand and will also find sufficiently interesting to want to act on. This information can be seen on food labels and leaflets which are attached to products or are available in the store. In-store information in supermarkets often has recipe or meal suggestions which encourage consumers to make healthy choices.

## ▬ *Task* ▬

4 Some people do not enjoy eating fruit. Suggest four different ways in which fruit can be made attractive enough to encourage those people to increase their consumption. Include specific examples of the fruit which is used in each of the four ways you suggest.

# The design studio

Another member of the product development team is the manager of the design studio, who works initially with the product development manager. The **product design manager** formulates a design brief for the design studio to work from when they are working on the packaging which will best suit the product. This brief could include a summary of the opportunity which exists for the development of a particular product, together with some information about the type of product. This helps the designers to get ideas about the best way to communicate to the consumer the value of the product.

The designers need detailed marketing information to make sure the packaging supports the product. The following questions help to gather this information:

▶ **purpose** – why this product and why now?
▶ **position in market** – economy line, standard or premium?
▶ **people** – who is it for: men, women, families, children, age, socio-economic group?
▶ **personality** – traditional, ethnic, luxurious, fun, diet-related, nutrition.

Having decided which from this list best describes the product and the market, the design studio has a **profile**. An example of such a profile could be for a sandwich called 'The Bushman's Bite'. The product development team have decided to try a new filling made of crocodile meat, morello cherry and yoghurt.

---

*The bushman's bite – profile*

**Purpose**
▶ To give an upmarket feel to a sandwich, in that the filling is very different.
▶ To increase market share of the £5.2 million a day spent on sandwiches in the UK.

**Position**
▶ Premium with a luxury, 'different' image, but affordable at £1.25 for a 'new experience'.

**People**
▶ Adventurous, informed, relaxed.
▶ Male 20–35 age range, professional young female.

**Personality**
▶ Modern, approachable, easy going, individual.

---

The packaging and the information given on the packaging for this product would be developed to emphasize the qualities identified in the profile. Other things which the designers must take account of include:
▶ corporate identity (the image which the company has)
▶ consistency of where information appears on the packaging. If the same information, such as the ingredients list, nutrition information, weight and so on, always appears in the same place on a manufacturer's products, customer confidence is increased.

The designers must view the packaging design from the customers' perspective. This involves analysing possible designs for customer reactions. It covers all aspects of the design from the style of the typeface, colours (number and combination), illustrations and the consumer information to be used.

The typeface and colours used communicate a message about the product. For example if a product is a 'standard' product, i.e. one which is in every-day use, such as a bag of sugar, or a sliced loaf, the packaging is functional, 'no-nonsense' and makes the product easy to identify. In addition the package used by producers and manufacturers of these types of products changes very little which means the consumer chooses with confidence knowing the product remains the same.

If the product is in the economy range, the consumer is more likely to have confidence in its relative value and potential for saving money if the packaging is plain and ordinary, with limited use of colour or one colour only in the design. The consumer will know that the price of the product is not **loaded** to cover the cost of expensive package design. The image will fit the consumer's expectation.

If the product is classed as a premium product, that is one with luxury appeal, the consumer expects the packaging to be elegant, sophisticated and to have the style which is associated with the product. There are many ways of achieving this style, for example through a particular image (often supported by advertising in the media) and/or through the use of colour (some colours and colour combination are seen to be elegant and give a luxury feel).

## Task

5 The photo below shows examples of economy, standard and premium products.
  a Which one is which?
  b How did you know?

# Packaging

## How do consumers react to packaging?

There are many ways in which consumers may react to packaging. Here are some examples.

▶ Where the packaging must fulfil a purpose, for example a product which is poured from the container or one where a ring pull is the means of opening, the consumer must have confidence that it will work (it must be **fit for the purpose**). The container must pour without dripping and the ring pull must open the product effectively and safely. If the container drips when it pours or the ring pull does not open the tin, the consumer does not feel kindly disposed to that product and may not buy it again. Consumers expect things to work as they are intended.

▶ If a basic product such as a standard or economy commodity is 'overdressed' by its packaging, the consumer will be disappointed with the contents and may think they are overpriced.

▶ If a premium product such as a luxury food is 'underdressed' by its packaging the consumer may think it is too expensive and it will not sell.

The relationship between consumers and packaging may sometimes be called **people and price points**. This means that people for whom the product is intended will accept the cost of a product only if they think the product is likely to be worth that price. If, for example, the consumer has great expectations of a product which appears to have a rather low price for that type of product, the consumer may suspect that their expectations will not be realized and therefore will not buy the product. Similarly, a product which consumers expect to be offered at a particular price point, will not sell well if the actual price is very different – whether much lower or much higher.

## Considerations for packaging design

Other aspects which must be taken into account include:

▶ **environmental issues** – generally manufacturers try to take a 'protective' view about this. They try to protect the environment whilst, at the same time, making sure that products are not damaged between the production line and the consumer's 'point of use'.

▶ **the properties of the food** which is being packaged; for example food containing fat must have air-tight packaging because oxygen in the air could cause the fat to become rancid; foods which are dried must be packed in moisture-proof material. Examples of packaging materials are given on pages 36–7.

▶ **how the product will be processed, distributed and stored** – this includes understanding the effects of temperature, pH, the ingredients used (recipe formulation and ratio of ingredients) and so on, and ensuring that the packaging chosen will keep that product in first-class condition.

▶ **the type of product** – some products are packaged on a tray-type base and covered with a 'slide-off' type of packing. This slide-off is called a sleeve. Depending on the type of product the sleeve is a 'half sleeve' or a 'full sleeve'. Where the consumer needs to see the product e.g. fresh fish pieces, the sleeve would be a half-sleeve which leaves room for the product to be seen. Where the consumer might be 'put-off' by the appearance of the 'cold' product e.g. many cook-chill ready meals, a full sleeve is used, with an 'encouraging' photograph of the product on it.

## What does all this mean for a design studio?

Most manufacturers and retailers have so many products being developed, relaunched, extended or modified at any one time that the in-house design team do not have time to carry out the whole design process for the packaging of any one particular product. This work is frequently given to an external design company.

The design studio puts together a detailed design brief for the external company. Each person in the design studio is handling a number of products at any one time. Their task is to ask the external company to produce two or three different ideas, with two or three different versions of each idea for each product. The normal time scale allowed for this is about two weeks. A choice is made by the design studio team and then this is worked on by the external company, which produces a final version at the end of about four weeks. This final version is presented to the design studio and to other members of the product development team.

During the presentation a detailed break-down of the packaging is presented in a number of different ways, for example in design-sheet form and in model form, depending on what is most appropriate. Examples of how similar products are packaged by competitors are often part of the presentation. After eight weeks, all the artwork details, including photographs, illustrations etc. are put together in a detailed specification and they become the blue-print for the printer. It is just like concept generation for a design-and-make task in school!

## What information appears on the packaging?

The illustration of the mayonnaise label shows different ways of communicating information to the consumer. The information on the packaging of a product may include:

▶ the product name and any sub-title which might be appropriate, such as Asparagus Ravioli, fresh Italian pasta
▶ the product weight
▶ a product description
▶ an ingredients list (in descending order of weight or volume)
▶ cooking instructions, guidelines
▶ serving suggestions
▶ storage guidelines
▶ nutrition information
▶ flashes, particular needs met by the product , such as 'Suitable for vegetarians', 'Suitable for home freezing' etc.
▶ logos which show that the product is part of a group of foods which are selected for a particular purpose – such as the 'Healthy Eating Symbol'
▶ environmental statements or symbols, for example, which means the packaging is made from recycled materials or can be recycled

▶ any legal advice or particular warning, for example, 'This product has been partially boned, a small bone still remains', 'This product contains nuts'
▶ manufacturer's name and address
▶ country of manufacture
▶ batch number
▶ bar code
▶ price
▶ 'display until' or 'use by' dates
▶ opening instructions.

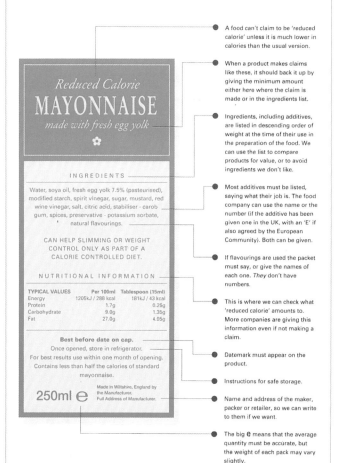

Source – MAFF and Foodsense, © Crown copyright

■ An example of the types of information given on food labels

# Information about food labelling and advertising

The **Food Advisory Committee** (**FAC**) made recommendations in 1989 about nutrition claims made in labelling and advertising of food products. Many of these recommendations are not legally required but manufacturers are advised to use them so that consumers are given helpful information in a consistent way. The nutrition claims covered by the guidelines include the following words:

- ▶ low
- ▶ no-added
- ▶ free of/without
- ▶ source
- ▶ increased
- ▶ reduced
- ▶ more/less
- ▶ high/rich.

The following table shows the details.

| | *Low* | *No added* | *X free* |
|---|---|---|---|
| Fat | No more than 5 g in either a normal serving of food for which this is more than 100 g or 100 ml *or* in 100 g or 100 ml of a food for which the normal serving is less than this amount. In the case of a food naturally low in fat the claim must be made in the form 'a low fat food'. | | No more than 0.15 g per 100 g or 100 ml |
| Saturates | No more than 3 g in either a normal serving of a food for which this is more than 100 g or a 100 ml *or* in 100 g or 100 ml of food for which the normal serving is less than this amount. In the case of a food naturally low in saturates the claim must be made in the form 'a low saturates food'. | | No more than 0.1 g per 100 g or 100 ml |
| Sugar(s) | No more than 5 g in either a normal serving of a food for which this is more than 100 g or 100 ml *or* in 100 g or 100 ml of a food for which the normal serving is less than this amount. In the case of food naturally low in sugar(s) the claim must be made in the form 'a low sugar(s) food'. | No sugars or foods composed mainly of sugars added to the food or to any of its ingredients | No more than 0.2 g per 100 g or 100 ml |
| Salt/ Sodium | No more than 40 mg in either a normal serving of a food for which this is more than 100 g or 100 ml *or* in 100 g or 100 ml of a food for which the normal serving is less than this amount. In the case of a food naturally low in salt/sodium the claim must be made in the form 'a low salt/sodium food'. | No salts or sodium shall have been added to the food or to any of its ingredients | No more than 5 mg per 100 g or 100 ml |

| | *Source* | *Increased* | *Rich* |
|---|---|---|---|
| Fibre | Either 3 g per 100 g or 100 ml or at least 3 g in the reasonable expected daily intake of the food. In the case of a food naturally high in fibre, the claim must take the form 'a high fibre food'. | At least 25% more than a similar food for which no claim is made *and* at least 3 g in either the reasonable daily intake of a food for which this is lower than 100 g or 100 ml *or* in 100 g or 100 ml. | Either at least 6 g per 100 g or 100 ml *or* at least 6 g of the reasonably expected daily intake of the foods. |

# More information about claims

There are two main formats. They are:
▶ the 'Group 1 Declaration', which gives the minimum amount of information and is also known as 'Big 4' and must cover nutrient and amount.

### Group 1

| | |
|---|---|
| energy | kJ and kcal |
| protein | g |
| carbohydrate | g |
| fat | g |

For example:

| NUTRITION INFORMATION | | |
|---|---|---|
| TYPICAL VALUES | PER 100g (3.5oz) | PER PACK |
| ENERGY | 1367 kJ. | 2173 kJ. |
| | 328 kcal | 521 kcal |
| PROTEIN | 13.8g | 21.9g |
| CARBOHYDRATE | 21.5g | 34.2g |
| FAT | 20.7g | 33.0g |
| PER PACK | **521** CALORIES | **33.0g** FAT |

▶ the 'Group 2 Declaration', which is also known as the '4 + 4 Declaration' or 'Big 4 and little 4'.

### Group 2

| | |
|---|---|
| energy | kJ and kcal |
| protein | g |
| carbohydrate | g |
|   of which: | |
|    – sugars | g |
| fat | g |
|   of which: | |
|    – saturates | g |
| fibre | g |
| sodium | g |

For example:

| NUTRITION | | |
|---|---|---|
| AVERAGE VALUES | PER **100g** | PER **239 g** 8.4oz ¹/₂ PACK |
| **ENERGY** | 510 kJ | 1215 kJ |
| | 120 kcal | 285 kcal |
| **PROTEIN** | 9.0 g | 21.4 g |
| **CARBOHYDRATE** | 5.1 g | 12.1 g |
| OF WHICH SUGARS | Trace | Trace |
| **FAT** | 7.5 g | 17.9 g |
| OF WHICH SATURATES | 4.6 g | 10.9 g |
| **FIBRE** | 0.6 g | 1.4 g |
| **SODIUM** | 0.8 g | 1.9 g |

# What amounts must be declared?

The amounts declared must be per 100 g or 100 ml of the food. If a vitamin and/or a mineral claim is made then an additional declaration per serving or per portion is required.

# Food for particular nutritional uses (PARNUT foods)

These include foods that are suitable for people with coeliac disease, for whom a declaration of gluten content is necessary, and foods for people with diabetes, for whom declarations are also necessary. As an example, references to fructose often appear on diabetic foods.

# Where do trade marks, copyright and patents fit in?

A manufacturer can protect a design and/or a product by registering it in such a way as to prevent someone else from producing something which is exactly the same.

Trade marks, copyright and patents are all ways in which design protection can be assured.

■ Manufacturers use registered trade marks to prevent their products being copied

## ▬ *Task* ▬

1 a Investigate the specific nutritional needs of a person with coeliac disease.

  b Identify and describe a range of PARNUT foods which are produced specifically for them.

# What is used to make packaging?

Different materials are used and are selected on the basis of which one is best suited to preserve the desired qualities of the product. The three main reasons for packaging are:
1 to protect a product from damage or contamination by micro-organisms and air, moisture, toxins etc.
2 to keep the product together, to contain it (i.e. so that it doesn't spill)
3 to identify the product.

These reasons summarize the functions which packaging must fulfil. In more detail the functions are:

1 *Protecting the product:*
▶ The product must be protected against mechanical forces such as compression (being squashed), vibration, impact or collision with another object. (Good examples of products which have a delicate structure are fruits which need to be protected by a more rigid structure such as a can or a laminated foil container.)
▶ It must be protected against the climate, including conditions such as the application and/or absence of heat (high and low atmospheric temperatures), humidity, light, gases in the air etc.
▶ It must also be protected against micro-organisms, chemicals, soil, insects etc.

2 *Containing the product*
▶ Some products have difficult shapes and cannot be packaged easily, as, for example, some vegetables. What sometimes happens is that suppliers of a particular vegetable e.g. carrots, develop a particular type of plant which yields carrots which are smaller and straighter in form than the normal variety, so that they can fit into the cans used to contain canned carrots more easily.
▶ Some products, such as fruit juices and sauces, are liquid and could spill. These need to be contained in packaging which can hold them and be sealed to prevent spillage and loss.

3 *Identification*
On pages 32–5 there are details of the way in which information about the product is conveyed. There are regulations that govern what can be included in the identification, for example the way in which the name of the product is given can indicate how much of the main ingredients the product contains. Some fruit drinks labelled 'squash', for example, may contain little – if any – real fruit, whereas a drink labelled 'juice' must have a large proportion of fruit.

# The materials used

Packaging technology is constantly adapting and improving materials and methods to fulfil the three main functions. In early history natural materials such as wood and pottery were used and in relatively recent times glass, paper and metal were made and adapted for use as packaging. Synthetic materials such as cellulose and polythene were added to the list much more recently.

*Plastics*
Plastics are used to make different types of containers, some of which are rigid and some which are flexible.
▶ **Polyethylene terephthalate (PET)** is used to make bottles which are rigid and impermeable (will not let anything through). These bottles have advantages over glass bottles because they are lighter and will not break.
▶ **Polystyrene** can be made into trays and containers. The polystyrene is often expanded and pressed into shapes to hold cartons etc. Polystyrene is a poor conductor of heat and therefore can be used for insulated containers.
▶ **Polythene** may be low density or high density, has good water vapour resistance and is strong and relatively cheap. Low-density polythene will not withstand temperatures above 90 °C so for products such as 'boil in the bag', where a higher temperature is an essential part of the process, high-density polythene must be used. Polythene allows some oxygen to pass through it, so where this is not desirable, as in vacuum packaging, or for a product which deteriorates in the presence of oxygen, such as foods containing fat which can become rancid in the presence of oxygen, a film of another material is bonded to it. This is called a laminate.

▶ **Polyamide**, a type of nylon, is often used as a laminate.

▶ **Cellulose films** are used in a range of densities which have different characteristics – for example some are moisture proof and some are not.

*Other materials*

▶ **Glass** has a number of disadvantages – it is heavy and breaks easily – but it is still used for many products. The shapes in which glass containers are made vary a great deal and can help to swell sales.

▶ **Paper** is still a popular packaging material, often used because it has a 'green' image and can be recycled easily. Examples include the trays for foods which can be microwaved – the paper or board is coated with a material which can withstand high temperatures up to 140°C. The coating material used is polypropylene.

■ Containers come in all sorts of shapes and sizes

## Tasks

Choose a commercial ready meal product and carry out the following activities using it.

2 a List the different types of information which appear on the packaging.

  b How much space does each piece of information take up?

  c Is a lot of detail included? Is this detail useful? Why?

  d Are any claims made? If so, what are they?

  e Is the information given clear? Is it easy to understand? What main messages are given about the product?

3 Could any aspect of the packaging be improved? How? (Consider convenience, consumer appeal, safety, amount, i.e. too much, not enough, just right, function – is it effective?)

4 Cook and taste the product and then answer the following questions;

  a Is the product what you were led to expect from the information on the packaging?

  b Does it meet any claims made for it, for example crisp, flavoursome, filling etc?

  c Were the cooking and serving guidelines helpful? How?

  d Would you buy the product again? Why?

These tasks illustrate the importance of 'pleasing' the consumer when you are designing and making your products in school.

To extend this task you might consider how the product could be improved for you and then design and make the improved version.

Milk and bread are two examples of basic foods which form a large part of most people's daily intake of food. The tables show:

**a** how much milk and bread and related products people ate in the period 1992–1994

**b** how much was spent per person per week on each food.

### Consumption and expenditure for milk and cream 1992–4 – per person per week

| | Consumption | | | Expenditure | | |
|---|---|---|---|---|---|---|
| | 1992 | 1993 | 1994 | 1992 | 1993 | 1994 |
| | (ml) | | | (pence) | | |
| Milk | 2111 | 2039 | 2054 | 116.1 | 116.4 | 113.4 |
| Yoghurt and fromage frais | 122 | 122 | 122 | 23.2 | 24.3 | 23.9 |
| Cream | 18 | 18 | 16 | 4.2 | 4.4 | 4.1 |
| Total milk and cream | 2220 | 2179 | 2192 | 143.5 | 145.1 | 141.2 |

Source – MAFF, *National Food Survey*, 1994

### Consumption and expenditure for bread 1992–4 – per person per week

| | Consumption | | | Expenditure | | |
|---|---|---|---|---|---|---|
| | 1992 | 1993 | 1994 | 1992 | 1993 | 1994 |
| | (ml) | | | (pence) | | |
| White bread (standard loaves) | 367 | 376 | 390 | 24.5 | 24.2 | 23.7 |
| White premium and softgrain bread | 62 | 54 | 49 | 4.7 | 4.0 | 3.5 |
| Brown bread | 93 | 94 | 83 | 8.3 | 8.2 | 7.3 |
| Wholemeal bread | 109 | 105 | 104 | 9.4 | 8.8 | 8.6 |
| Other bread (incl. rolls and prepared sandwiches) | 123 | 128 | 133 | 22.5 | 23.8 | 25.1 |
| Total bread | 755 | 757 | 758 | 69.4 | 69.0 | 68.2 |

Source – MAFF, *National Food Survey*, 1994

## Milk

Nutritionally, milk is an almost perfect food. The bar chart shows what one pint of milk contributes, as a

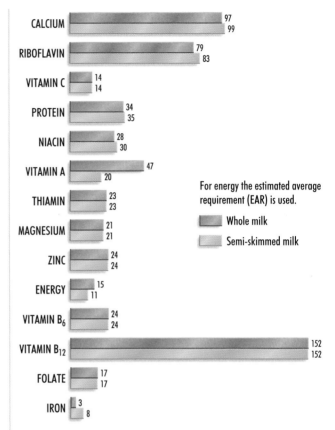

For energy the estimated average requirement (EAR) is used.

▮ Whole milk

▯ Semi-skimmed milk

| Nutrient | Whole milk | Semi-skimmed milk |
|---|---|---|
| CALCIUM | 97 | 99 |
| RIBOFLAVIN | 79 | 83 |
| VITAMIN C | 14 | 14 |
| PROTEIN | 34 | 35 |
| NIACIN | 28 | 30 |
| VITAMIN A | 47 | 20 |
| THIAMIN | 23 | 23 |
| MAGNESIUM | 21 | 21 |
| ZINC | 24 | 24 |
| ENERGY | 15 | 11 |
| VITAMIN B$_6$ | 24 | 24 |
| VITAMIN B$_{12}$ | 152 | 152 |
| FOLATE | 17 | 17 |
| IRON | 3 | 8 |

■ Nutrient contribution to the average UK diet made by 1 pint of milk, as a percentage of the dietary reference values (DRVs)

percentage of the dietary reference values (DRVs). On average, almost 28 per cent of our daily calcium intake comes from milk. Milk is presented in so many different forms that everyone has at least one form available to them which meets their needs.

The majority of milk is **heat-treated**. **Pasteurization** is the most popular method. Other heat treatments include **ultra-heat treatment (UHT)** and **sterilization**. The procedure of heating milk that is called the **high-temperature short time (HTST)** process involves heating the milk to not less than 71.7°C for at least 15 seconds.

Ultra-heat treated milk (UHT) is a very useful 'standby' because it can be stored at ambient temperature (i.e. room temperature) and need not be refrigerated. It has a shelf-life of several months and is always stamped with a 'best before' date. When opened it must be kept in the refrigerator and used within five days.

UHT milk is produced by the sterilization of homogenized milk, it is packed into sterile cartons in

| Top | What is it? |
|---|---|
| | **Silver top**<br>Whole milk – 3.9% fat<br>1 pint contains 23 grams fat and 375 kJ (66 kcal)<br>Recommended by nutritionists as part of staple diet of all children under five |
| | **Red top**<br>The same as silver top but homogenized (fat has been evenly distributed throughout milk, therefore no creamy top) |
| | **Gold top**<br>Rich creamy taste – 4.9% fat<br>1 pint contains 29 grams fat and approximately 340 kJ (80 kcal) |
| | **Red and silver striped top**<br>Semi-skimmed milk (half the fat of silver and red top) – 1.5 to 1.8% fat<br>1 pint contains 9–10.5 grams fat and approximately 197 kJ (47 kcal) |
| | **Blue and silver checked top**<br>Skimmed milk (almost all fat removed) – 0.1% fat<br>1 pint contains almost no fat, 141 kJ (33 kcal)<br>Vitamins A and D are lost as a result of skimming off most of the fat |

a completely sterile environment and heat-sealed.

The cartons are made from polyethylene, which is laminated (coated) with a layer each of paper, plastic and aluminium foil. The cartons do not allow oxygen to pass through to the milk, thus preventing the fat in the milk from becoming rancid.

### Identifying different types of milk

Doorstep milk, which is sold in bottles, can usually be identified by the different coloured tops.

Many consumers now buy their milk with the rest of their groceries when shopping in a supermarket or other type of shop. The same range of milk as that offered by doorstep delivery is available. The milk is usually packed in cartons or plastic flask-type containers and is available from small to large amounts, for example from 275 ml ($\frac{1}{2}$ pint cartons) to 2 litre plus (3$\frac{1}{2}$ pint plus) flasks. Other forms of milk that are available include:

▸ evaporated milk
  • concentrated, sterilized milk
  • canned
▸ condensed milk
  • concentrated milk with added sugar
  • not sterilized, but the high concentration of sugar acts as a preservative
  • canned
▸ dried milk
  • can be whole or skimmed
  • homogenized, heat-treated and then dried
  • must be treated as fresh milk when hydrated (i.e. water added; reconstituted)
▸ UHT milk
  • sterilized homogenized milk
  • unopened shelf life of several months, stored at ambient temperatures
▸ flavoured milk
  • gaining in popularity
  • wide variety of flavours and consistencies
  • some is long life (UHT or sterilized), some fresh
  • three most popular flavours are strawberry, banana, chocolate.

## Tasks

1 Carry out a survey in school to discover:
  a how many people drink flavoured milks
  b what are the favourite flavours with those people.
  Record the results. Collate the results. Which is the most popular flavour?

2 Make a flavoured drink with milk, using the most popular flavour you have identified. This is easily carried out using a liquidizer. If there isn't one flavour which came out as the definite favourite, try a banana liquidized with milk, with cocoa sprinkled on the top.

# Milk products

Butter and cheese are obvious examples of milk products. Cream is another milk product which has many uses in the design and production of food products. The reason for this is that there are many forms of cream, including:

▶ single
▶ double
▶ whipping
▶ soured (including crème fraîche)
▶ half-cream
▶ clotted.

These differ mainly by:

▶ how thick they are
▶ the fat content.

The table gives a description of each type.

*Cooking with cream*

**1** Because of the high percentage of fat in most creams the protein content is reduced. On coagulation proteins forms a skin, therefore the less protein, the less chance of a skin forming. This means that when cream is added to a sauce there is less likelihood of a skin forming which could spoil the consistency of the sauce.

**2** Cream is less likely to produce a curdled result when added to a mixture containing an acid.

**3** When whipping cream:

▶ the fat content of the cream must not be below 30 per cent
▶ keep it at a temperature of 7°C or lower
▶ foam (see page 71) is not produced when 'warmer' cream is whipped.
▶ over-whipping makes the fat globules stick together, resulting in a butter-like product.

| Type | Fat content | Uses |
|---|---|---|
| Half cream | 12% | – Light, pouring<br>Will not whip |
| Single cream | 18% | – Light, pouring<br>Will not whip<br>Will not freeze, unless mixed into a cooked dish<br>Can make soups and quiche mixtures rich |
| Extra thick | 18% | – Homogenized to make thick consistency<br>As for single cream |
| Soured cream | 18% | – Made from fresh single cream<br>Culture is added to produce distinctive flavour<br>Will not whip<br>Used in sweet and soured dishes e.g. pork stroganoff, many cheesecake recipes |
| Crème fraîche | 30% | – Fresh cream with a 'sour' taste<br>Will not whip<br>Used as a pouring cream and in some mixtures such as salad dressings |
| Whipping cream | 35% | – Will double in volume when whipped<br>Will freeze in whipped state, frozen life about two months<br>Used in mousses, soufflés, decorations and fillings |
| Double cream | 48% | – Will whip easily<br>Will freeze in whipped state, frozen life about two months<br>Very versatile in use. |
| Extra thick double cream | 48% | – Homogenized to make it thick.<br>Will not whip.<br>Will not freeze successfully. |
| Clotted cream | 55% | – Can be frozen for up to one month<br>Not good for cooking because it separates easily<br>Served with puddings, scones (for cream tea) |

Task

3 a Examine the fat content of double cream and whipping cream by looking at the text and at some cartons of creams in shops.

  b Find two different recipes which use cream (mousses and cold soufflés are examples).

  c Decide whether either of these creams could be used in the recipe. Explain why.

## Yoghurt

Yoghurt is a good example of a **by-product** from milk production. It is a 'healthy alternative' to cream and is extremely useful because:

▶ it is a use of an over production of milk i.e. it uses up a glut

▶ it extends the shelf life of milk from a few days to some weeks.

### How is yoghurt made?

The flow diagram shows the ingredients, processes and safety and quality checks which must be carried out during manufacture.

### Market opportunities

The popularity of yoghurt increased ten-fold in the UK from 0.4 kg per person per year in 1966 to 4.1 kg per person per year in 1989. There has been a levelling out in growth in recent years but yoghurt production is still a dynamic market for manufacturers. There are many market opportunities for:

▶ developing new products

▶ modifying existing products

▶ extending product ranges

▶ creating products to suit different sectors of the market, such as low-fat, slimming, different cultures etc.

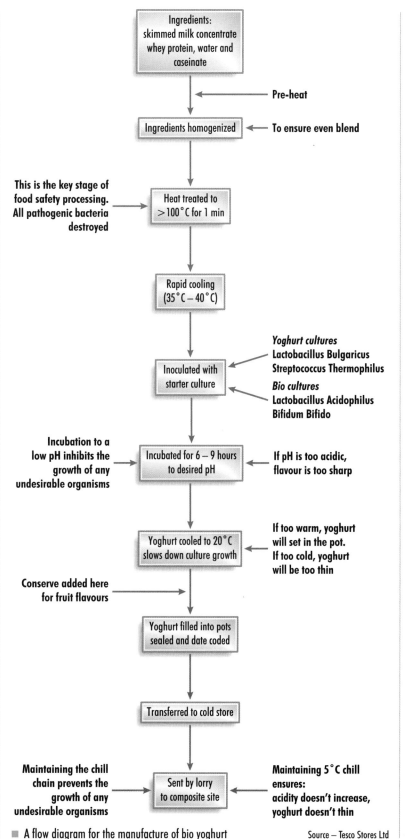

■ A flow diagram for the manufacture of bio yoghurt

Source – Tesco Stores Ltd

*The consumer and yoghurt*

There are many benefits to the consumer, including:

▶ substantial evidence to show that yoghurt can be eaten by people with lactose intolerance (those people who cannot drink milk because they have allergic reactions to the lactose in milk)

▶ the attractive image of a low-fat product

▶ the convenience of the portion-sizes available. For example, individual portions of 150 g, family servings of 500 g and family packs of four or more individual portions packaged together (often using a system called **form-fill**)

▶ the large choice of available yoghurt, including stirred, set, fruit flavouring and yoghurt separated from each other in same pack.

— *Task* —

4  Make your own yoghurt.

*Equipment needed*
▶ a cooking thermometer
▶ a wide-necked Thermos or other flask
▶ a glass disc (or other device to stop the milk boiling over)

*Recipe*

570 ml (1 pint) milk

1 teaspoon *natural* yoghurt (fruit flavoured or sweetened yoghurt will not do)

*Method*
1  Bring the milk to the boil in a saucepan. Put the glass disc (or other device) in the pan.
2  Reduce heat and simmer for 35 minutes. The milk will reduce, to about 400 ml ($\frac{3}{4}$ pint).
3  Tip the milk into a clean jug. Stand jug in cold water for five minutes.
4  Leave the jug in the cold water. Put the thermometer in the milk (make sure it is clean and dry). Keep the jug in the cold water until the temperature of the milk gets to 49°C.
5  Put the yoghurt in the flask. Add about a quarter of the milk and stir. Add the rest of the milk, stirring all the time.
6  Put the lid on the flask. Leave for at least six hours. Taste the yoghurt. Add fruit or other flavourings if you wish.
7  Store the resulting yoghurt in the refrigerator. For safety check everything is clean and the thermometer is accurate.

# Ice cream

Ice cream is another spin-off of milk production. The final product is a foam in which air cells are distributed within the partially frozen continuous phase of an oil-in-water **emulsion**. Dairy ice cream contains milk and cream and has sugar, emulsifiers, stabilizers and flavourings added to it. Ice cream regulations determine whether ice cream can be described as dairy ice cream. They require dairy ice cream to contain not less than 7.5 per cent milk-solids-not-fat (called SNF in the industry) and not less than 5 per cent milk fat. Non-dairy ice cream is mostly made from skimmed milk and vegetable fat.

*How is ice cream produced?*

▶ The ingredients are mixed and heated to dissolve sugar and sterilize the mix.

▶ The mix is then frozen rapidly to avoid large crystals forming which spoil the texture.

▶ The mixture is stirred vigorously to get air into the mixture. This increases the volume of the mixture (called **overrun** in the industry).

*What is the difference between hard and soft ice cream?*

▶ Hard ice cream must have an overrun of 100 per cent (the basic mixture must double its volume during mixing), compared with soft ice cream where the overrun must be around 50 per cent (it has less air mixed into the mixture).

▶ Hard ice cream contains more fat (often 12 per cent compared with 6 per cent in soft ice cream).

▶ Hard ice cream can be cut into blocks and particular shapes to make a variety of products.

*Points of care in ice cream production*

▶ Ingredients must be balanced, for example too much milk powder may lead to a gritty texture as the sugar in milk (lactose) may form crystals.

▶ Stabilizers are added to give the product body and improve its ability to remain in a frozen state.

▶ Emulsifiers and stabilizers (such as pectins, gums, carageenans, modified cellulose) are added to prevent large ice crystals forming.

*Ice cream production and designing and making products in the classroom*

Ice cream is a popular product. In 1994 4p per person per week was spent on ice cream outside the home. At first sight this does not seem to be a

large market but in fact it is. Why is this?
▶ 'Per person' means an average figure for every member of the population.
▶ 'Per week' means 52 weeks of the year (including winter months).

Some important conclusions can be drawn.
▶ A considerable number of people spent a lot more than 4p per week on ice cream.
▶ Ice cream sales have seasonal highs, for example sales rise during warmer months.

These facts give a reasonably reliable indication of how profitable ice cream products are.

Ice cream provides rich opportunities for product development. For example, the well-known brand Wall's Cornetto gave rise to a number of similar products based on the ice cream being 'contained' and packaged in a wafer-type outside. The wafer is cooked flat and then formed into a cornet shape when still warm. As it cools the cornet shape becomes firm and strong enough to hold the ice cream filling.

This process can be carried out in school using a brandy snap type mixture and also melted chocolate. In the case of melted chocolate, a paper cornet is made first. This is then coated with two or three layers of melted chocolate which are then allowed to cool. The paper is carefully peeled off when the chocolate is set. The cornet can then be filled with ice cream or another soft mixture.

■ There is a wide variety of ice cream products available

Other forms in which ice cream is marketed include blocks or other shapes of ice cream dipped in chocolate, chocolate and nut mixtures, fruit purées and so on.

## ▬ *Tasks* ▬

**5 a** Identify four different ice cream products. Include two which are copies of well known unfrozen chocolate bars.
  **b** Choose two of these products including one of the chocolate bar copies. Compare them for:
   ▶ price
   ▶ appearance and structure
   ▶ taste
   ▶ nutritional composition
   ▶ how appropriate they are to serve as a dessert in a meal.

**6** Cold desserts are popular parts of meals. Imagine you have been asked to design and make a low-fat cold dessert which uses milk and/or a milk product.
  **a** (i) Research recipes for cold puddings which use milk and/or milk products.
   (ii) Research the nutritional composition of appropriate ingredients.
  **b** Produce a design sheet which shows:
   (i) the product you have chosen and why you have chosen it
   (ii) the recipe formulation and the nutritional composition
   (iii) a sequenced flow of the activities involved in production, which includes safety and quality checks to be made
   (iv) the ratio of one ingredient with another in graphical form (e.g. bar chart, pie chart). Use a computer if possible.
  **c** Make a one-off version of your product.
  **d** Explain on the design sheet what must be done to produce large numbers of the product that are consistent in shape, size and quality.
  **e** Mock-up an advertisement for your product. Include either a photograph of the finished dish or a 3D model representation made using computer-aided design (CAD).

## Bread

Bread is a staple food in most people's diets in the UK. However, although the consumption of bread rises each year, the figures on page 38 show that the market was less profitable for manufacturers in 1994 than it was in 1992. In 1992 the figure for bread sales, per person per week, was 69.4p compared with 68.2p per person per week in 1994. The reason for this is that over 80 per cent of bread sales take place in the large retailing sector (supermarkets and the large multiple bakery firms) at the expense of the high street baker.

In the early 1990s a **price war** arose in this sector, which resulted in the price of a standard white loaf being reduced to below what it cost to produce (i.e. the standard white loaf was used as a 'loss leader'). This meant that although consumption figures rose there was a fall in the actual value of the bread sector.

### What does the future hold for this product?

Research shows that bread products are very popular with the consumer and that there is an ever-increasing demand for new products and flavours.

One example of a profitable application of bread is the **sandwich**. Figures show that eight out of ten people in the UK eat sandwiches regularly. The Federation of Master Bakers discovered that 31 million sandwiches are eaten in London every week. Mintel, a market intelligence company, reports that 800 million sandwiches are sold annually through a variety of sandwich bars, petrol forecourt shops and retailers.

Other examples of profitable applications of bread include pizzas, continental breads and varieties such as pitta bread and naan bread. New bread types such as herb and sun-dried tomato, Turkestan, ciabatta, muesli, olive and focaccia with rosemary and basil are proving popular with consumers and are becoming profitable for producers.

### Using this information in school – a case study

The winning Independent Bread Baker of 1994, John Foster, is the managing director of a family firm which is always looking out for innovative bread recipes which meet its customers' needs. Seventy-five per cent of the firm's customers are wholesalers which means that the market potential is large.

The staff of this firm are encouraged to take part in product development by brainstorming ideas of exciting new bread 'applications'. The staff have a wide age range and have different qualifications and experience, which means that the ideas generated are likely to meet the needs of a great variety of consumers.

This approach has brought positive results to the business because, although some of the ideas are a bit impractical, many others are good and it is worth making up recipes for testing in the kitchen.

By exploring the theme 'New ideas for bread products', much can be discovered about how bread is made and what a versatile product it is. This in turn can provide interesting possibilities for designing and making bread products.

## The ingredients of bread

Before starting to design and make bread products it is important to understand how and why the ingredients combine.

1 The basic ingredients are strong flour, liquid, salt and yeast. A basic recipe is: 500 g strong plain flour, 2 level tsp salt, 20 g fresh yeast, 300 ml water, 25 g fat or 2 tbsp oil.
2 During mixing, water is absorbed into the mixture (the ingredients become **hydrated** with the water). The flour proteins (gliadin and glutenin) form **gluten** when hydrated. Gluten gives the dough elasticity, which means that it will stretch.
3 The yeast acts with the sugars to produce carbon dioxide ($CO_2$) and some alcohol (which explains the 'beery' smell of bread during processing). This is the fermentation process.
4 The carbon dioxide causes the dough to rise. The gluten surrounding the gas bubbles stretches to produce the risen quality of the dough.
5 The fermentation process depends on the yeast being given the conditions which allow it to grow. These conditions are moisture (supplied by the liquid in the recipe), food (supplied by sugars – either those naturally occurring in the ingredients or sometimes by the addition of a small amount of sugar to the recipe) and a warm temperature.
6 The temperature range at which the yeast grows (and thus produces the carbon dioxide necessary to raise the dough) is 24–40 °C. The liquid used to hydrate the dough should be around 37 °C (blood heat).

Controlling the temperature is critical because yeast is killed at 54 °C and above and becomes inactive (does not grow) below 10 °C. Details are shown in the table in the next column.

## Producing bread

1 The dough must have **proving** or rising periods in warm conditions to allow adequate gas to be produced. The best temperature for this is around 32 °C.
2 The dough is kneaded during the rising period to make sure the bubbles of gas become fairly uniform in size, otherwise a poor texture and

### Table of dough temperatures

| °C | |
|---|---|
| 0 | Freezing point |
| 4 | Temperature for refrigerated storage of yeast |
| 10 | Cold or cool room temperature for slow |
| 15 | fermentation of dough |
| 21 | Surrounding or room temperature for normal |
| 23.5 | fermentation of dough |
| 24 | |
| 26 | |
| 27 | Temperature of dough during fermentation |
| 28 | |
| 32 | |
| 37 | (Blood heat) |
| 38 | Temperatures for doughing liquid |
| 41 | |
| 43 | |
| 54 | Yeast is killed |
| 100 | Approximate *interior* temperature of loaf when drawn from the oven |

uneven crumb size will result in the baked product.
3 The dough is shaped or tinned before baking.
4 The oven temperature for baking should be around 230 °C. The interior temperature of the dough rises during the cooking time to about 100 °C which is what it should be when the baked product is taken out of the oven.
5 During the baking, changes take place at particular temperatures, e.g. at 65 °C starch begins to gelatinize; proteins coagulate at 75 °C.
6 The outside of the product reaches a much higher temperature than the interior and this produces attractive changes such as the brown crust on the outside of a loaf (the Maillard reaction). This takes place as a result of reactions between carbohydrate (actually a reducing sugar) and protein in the dough. The reaction is also called carbonyl-amine browning. This type of browning increases with an increase in pH and temperature.
7 Another change brought about during baking is that the starch changes to dextrin by a process called **dextrinization**. This causes a crust to form on the outside of the bread product and also causes some browning.

## Project

Develop you own ideas for applications of bread. A suitable starting point could be the following brief.

As part of a 'Children in Need' week, a team of four students in the Food Technology group are going to design and make midday lunch packs with a difference. The packs are to be on sale in the entrance hall of school between 12.30 pm and 1.30 pm.

Researching and planning the task could be team activities carried out at least one week before the packs go on sale.

1 What research should be carried out?
   a Consider the five Ws: Who? What? When? Where? Why?
   b Make notes. Decide on specific activities for each member of the group.
   c Look at what is already available. How can you fulfil the 'different' aspects of the brief?
   d What about cost? Investigate the costs of a variety of existing products which would fit the situation.
   e Brainstorm the following suggestions:
      ▸ The sale will be carried out on two different occasions.
      ▸ For the first occasion design and make products using bought breads as a basis.
      ▸ For the second occasion design and make products using a bread type which you make using your understanding of how successful bread products are achieved.
   During brainstorming you should consider all the aspects of the situation, such as timing, costings, the five Ws etc.
2 Draw up **criteria** for the tasks for the two different occasions. Set **specifications** for the products you are thinking of. The criteria are those aspects of the task which have to be met, for example products that are suitable for lunch packs with a difference. Details of types of products should be included, for example they must be capable of being eaten in the hand. The specifications are the precise recipe formulations and ratios and processing methods required to make good quality products.

Here are some ideas to help.

## Using bought breads as a base

---

*Croustades with savoury fillings*

These involve using medium-cut sliced bread (or try rye bread for something different).
▸ Cut the crusts off each slice and roll the bread flat with a rolling pin.
▸ Melt butter with crushed garlic; brush the melted butter over the bread slices.
▸ Cut each slice into four squares, press each square very firmly into a very small tartlet tin. (This is quicker if you use a twelve-hole tin.)
▸ Bake at 180°C for 10–15 minutes until crisp and lightish brown in colour.
▸ The little cups (croustades) made in this way will keep for up to two weeks in an airtight container.
▸ Fill with a variety of savoury fillings for serving. Examples might include tinned mackerel beaten with a little cream and mayonnaise, cottage cheese and tomato purée, prawns and sour cream or crème fraîche, chopped chicken and curried mayonnaise.

---

*Bruschettas with savoury toppings*

Use a French stick loaf (either white or granary is suitable).
▸ Slice the loaf thinly into rounds. Brush each round with oil (use olive oil, or for a stronger flavour try toasted sesame oil). Put the rounds on a baking tray.
▸ Bake at 180°C for about 15–20 minutes or until crisp.
▸ Cover with a variety of toppings, for example:
   • a slice of tomato and basil leaves
   • cream cheese and slices of cucumber
   • chopped gherkins and peppers.
▸ Dribble a little oil over the toppings and season with salt and pepper.

## Making a product from scratch

Timing might be a difficulty here because making a product from scratch takes longer than using bought bread. The following idea might help speed things up.

> ### Short-time bread dough
>
> (This is a domestic version of the Chorleywood process.)
> Use a basic bread recipe using 675 g strong plain flour, 30 g fresh yeast, 15 g salt, approximately 400 ml liquid, 25 mg tablet ascorbic acid (available from chemists, sometimes called redoxon).
>
> ### How does this work?
>
> The ascorbic acid tablet must be dissolved in the warm liquid before being added to the yeast. The best temperature for the liquid is 32–36°C. The dough is mixed and kneaded very well and left in a warm place for 10 minutes.
>
> The dough must then be kneaded very thoroughly and vigorously, then shaped and left in a warm place for the second time for as long as time allows (up to about 30 minutes).

> ### What can be made with this dough?
>
> There are many applications. Try to be inventive to fulfil the 'different' aspect of the brief. Here are some ideas to get you started. The dough can be rolled out thinly, cut into small squares or rounds (one portion sizes) and covered with a variety of different combinations of ingredients such as onions, sliced and gently softened in oil and covered with grated cheese and a slice of tomato, or for a more simple product try brushing a little oil over the surface and then sprinkling with rock salt and herbs. The pieces should then be baked (190°C for 10–20 minutes).

3 Plan and make the products. Each person could plan and make one of the varieties for each task. Starting the task using bought breads will help to identify some of the things which must be resolved in order to be successful with the other task where timing will be more critical.

4 Devise a very simple solution for wrapping individual portions of each product. One solution that might fit the purpose is to use Clingfilm with a paper napkin attached to the product. Do not forget to add something to the selling price to cover the cost of wrapping.

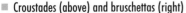 Croustades (above) and bruschettas (right)

■ Newly-baked loaves prior to depanning

■ A computer-controlled dough mixer at a French bakery. This fully automated machine has been dubbed the world's first 'thinking' dough mixer

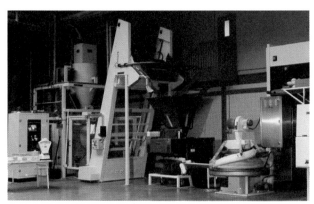

■ Large tunnel ovens are used for products ranging from Italian oven bottom country bread to high-output pan bread, as well as for many rolls, cakes, pastries and pies

■ Automatic ingredient feeds and a dough hoist linking the mixer and divider mean that no manual intervention is necessary

■ A tunnel oven with overhead prover

■ Conveyer systems are used to direct products to wherever they are needed, without the need for manual intervention

## Industrial applications?

It is well known that the smell of baking bread stimulates sales, as does the idea of bread which is produced daily using natural ingredients and traditional processing methods.

**a** Successful independent bakers take advantage of both those aspects by having freshly-baked products available six days a week. This often means the baker has to start work very early in the morning so that the first products are ready for sale at opening time, which is often as early as 7.30–8 a.m. The baker predicts how many of each product are likely to be sold and makes sufficient for that day's needs. This means that waste is cut to a minimum and the consumer gets fresh products every day.

**b** Other ways of providing freshly-baked bread for the consumer include:

 ▶ part-baked products which the consumer can take home and bake
 ▶ part-baked products which are delivered to high street retailers and small town general stores for baking on site. Where this system is successful the consumer gets used to being able to buy freshly-baked bread products (often still hot from the oven) throughout the day.

**c** Another development of this has recently been installed in about one third of a large retailer's stores, with plans for introduction into another 40 stores in the near future. This development produces 'fresh from the oven' bread and rolls throughout the day, so that a consumer has a fresh product, whatever time it is bought.

 The system is called the **Milton Keynes system**. It relies on the production of pre-formed yeast-raised baked goods which are stable at ambient temperatures and which can be subsequently baked to produce oven-fresh products.

 The system has been patented (patent number W095/30333). This is so that all the processing system information is protected and cannot be carried out by a competitor.

■ Trial products being sampled at Milton Keynes before the new breadmaking process was introduced in stores

**How *does the* Milton *Keynes system work*?**

▶ Dough pieces are baked so that the crumb is baked but the crust is not formed.

▶ Moisture is removed rapidly by vacuum whilst the dough pieces are still hot; this develops strength and structure in the crumb and the crust (the product is termed pre-formed at this stage).

▶ Pre-formed products are transported to an in-store bakery.

▶ The products are 'finished' (i.e. baked to produce a crisp, crusted browned product) to satisfy consumer demand throughout the day.

**d** Commercial production of pizza is another interesting application.

There are now many varieties of pizza on the market including deep-pan, border-free, lipped, snack-size, thin and crispy, wedge-shaped and French stick. They come fresh, frozen, chilled etc. Such a variety of production calls for a flexible production system, and such a system has been developed by a company called APV Baker.

The diagram below show a typical pizza plant which:

▶ mixes and forms dough

▶ cuts or presses dough to pizza bases which are uniform in weight and thickness

▶ proves and bakes

▶ cools (and freezes if necessary)

▶ de-pans the pizza bases with a suction depanner

▶ decorates and packs.

## Case study showing profitable pizza production

An Irish firm invested in their pizza plant in order to expand their share of this market. The main objective was to develop a high-quality product that would 'secure' its position in the market, and they succeeded in doing this.

The product is designed to be cooked on an open rack in the home oven, and it is sold frozen. Four styles of pizza bases are produced: deep-pan and thin, each in 9 inch and 12 inch diameters. The best-selling topping is bacon and mushroom.

Sampling during production takes places every hour to provide feedback about the effectiveness of the processing and to check that the quality control and safety checks are within tolerance limits. Samples are taken from

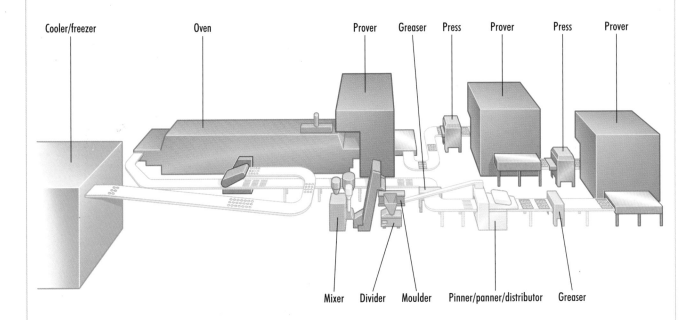

Cooler/freezer  Oven  Prover  Greaser  Press  Prover  Press  Prover

Mixer  Divider  Moulder  Pinner/panner/distributor  Greaser

the packing area and baked in the laboratory at the factory.

This company carries out new product development on site and recently introduced pizza sauces to serve with their pizzas. The sauces match the toppings so that a complete flavour profile is produced when pizza and sauce are eaten together.

The product development manager says, 'A pizza is a picture and must look like the illustration on the packaging.'

The company aims to produce a pizza with a good open texture, a crisp underside and a difference in mouth-feel between the crust and the topping or interior of the product. The photo below shows an example of the product.

## Task

7 Imagine you are marketing a deep-pan, six portion pizza topped with tomatoes, onions and black olives for home delivery by motorcycle.

a Design and make a sauce which could accompany this pizza. Explain why this sauce is suitable.

b Explain how you would pack the sauce in order that it should travel safely without spilling and so that it is easy to serve.

c Suggest one other dish which could accompany the pizza and sauce. Explain:
  ▸ why this dish is suitable
  ▸ how it would be packed for home delivery.

■ 'A pizza is a picture . . .'

# 3.1 *Nutrients*

Nutrition is not always the main reason for manufacturers developing a product. However there are on the market many products with a nutrition 'message'.

## 'The Balance of Good Health'

From a nutritional point of view, the background against which people should make choices is 'The Balance of Good Health' which is based on the Government's eight guidelines for a healthy diet.

1 Enjoy your food.
2 Eat a variety of different foods.
3 Eat the right amount to be a healthy weight.
4 Eat plenty of food that is rich in starch and fibre.
5 Don't eat too much fat.
6 Don't eat sugary foods too often.
7 Look after the vitamins and minerals in your food.
8 If you drink alcohol keep within sensible limits.

## The five food groups

'The Balance of Good Health' is based on five food groups:
▶ bread, other cereals and potatoes
▶ fruit and vegetables
▶ milk and dairy foods
▶ meat, fish and alternatives
▶ foods containing fat and foods containing sugar.

The 'balanced plate' illustration shows the five groups. The size of the section which each group occupies shows how the intake of that food should be balanced with the other foods shown. The five groups are described in detail in the table opposite.

Other information that is available to consumers includes the use of symbols such as the Healthy Eating symbol shown on some of Sainsbury's foods. The symbol is not a legal claim, its purpose is to help people get a better balance into their diet.

■ The Healthy Eating symbol. This symbol is used on a wide range of Sainsbury's products that are generally low in fat, including bread, potatoes, pasta, breakfast cereals, fruit, vegetables, some poultry, fish, lean meat, low-fat dairy products and selected convenience foods such as sandwiches and ready meals

## — Task

1 A Cheddar cheese, smoked ham and lettuce sandwich was redesigned to reduce the fat and energy content by using slices of eating apple instead of the smoked ham and by using low-fat cheese instead of full-fat Cheddar cheese. The table below compares the energy and fat content of these sandwiches.

| | Energy | | Fat |
|---|---|---|---|
| | KJ | Kcal | g |
| Cheddar cheese, smoked ham and lettuce | 2072 | 495 | 31.7 |
| low fat Cheddar cheese, apple and lettuce | 1578 | 377 | 18.4 |

Redesign a bacon, lettuce and tomato (BLT) sandwich to reduce the energy and fat content. Use food tables or a suitable computer program to help you work out the nutritional values.

Fruit and vegetables

Bread, other cereals and potatoes

Meat, fish and alternatives

Foods containing fat
Foods containing sugar

Milk and dairy foods

■ The balanced plate

Source – Health Education Authority

## The five food groups

| | What's included | Main nutrients | Recommendations | Recommendations |
|---|---|---|---|---|
| Bread, other cereals and potatoes | 'Other cereals' means things like breakfast cereals, pasta, rice, oats, noodles, maize, millet and cornmeal. Beans and pulses can be eaten as part of this group. | Carbohydrate (starch) 'Fibre' (NSP*) Some calcium and iron B vitamins | Eat lots | Try to eat wholemeal, wholegrain, brown or high-fibre versions where possible. Try to avoid: • having them fried too often (e.g. chips) • adding too much fat (e.g. thickly spread butter, margarine or low-fat spread on bread • adding rich sauces and dressings (e.g. cream or cheese on pasta). |
| Fruit and vegatables | Fresh, frozen and canned fruit and vegetables and dried fruit. A glass of fruit juice can also contribute. Beans and pulses can be eaten as part of this group. | Vitamin C Carotenes Folates 'Fibre' (NSP*) and some carbohydrate | Eats lots. | Eat a wide variety of fruit and vegetables. Try to avoid: • adding fat or rich sauces to vegetables (e.g. carrots glazed with butter, roast parsnips) • adding sugar or syrupy dressings to fruit (e.g. stewed apple with sugar, chocolate sauce on banana). |
| Milk and dairy foods | Milk, cheese, yoghurt and fromage frais. This group does not include butter, eggs and cream. | Calcium Protein Vitamin B12 Vitamins A and D | Eat or drink moderate amounts and choose lower fat versions whenever you can. | 'Lower fat versions' means semi-skimmed or skimmed milk, low fat (0.1% fat) yoghurts or fromage frais, and lower fat cheeses (e.g. Edam, half-fat Cheddar, Camembert) Check the amount of fat by looking at the nutrient information on the labels. Compare similar products and choose the lowest – for example 8% fat fromage frais may be labelled low fat but is not actually the lowest available. |
| Meat, fish and alternatives | Meat, poultry, fish, eggs, nuts, beans and pulses. Meat includes bacon and salami and meat products such as sausages, beefburgers and pâté. These are all relatively high fat choices. Beans, such as canned baked beans and pulses are in this group. Fish included frozen and canned fish such as sardines and tune, fish fingers and fish cakes. | Iron Protein B vitamins, especially B12 Zinc Magnesium | Eat moderate amounts and choose lower fat versions whenever you can. | 'Lower fat version' means things like meat with the fat cut off, poultry without the skin and fish without batter. Cook these foods without added fat. Beans and pulses are good alternatives to meat as they are naturally very low in fat. |
| Foods containing fat, Foods containing sugar | Foods containing fat: margarine, butter, other spreading fat and low-fat spreads, cooking oils, oil-based salad dressings, mayonnaise, cream, chocolate, crisps, biscuits, pastries, cake, puddings, ice cream, rich sauces and gravies. Foods containing sugar: soft drinks, sweets, jam and sugar as well as foods such as cake, puddings, biscuits, pastries and ice cream. | Fat, including some essential fatty acids, but also some vitamins. Some products also contain salt or sugar. Sugar, with minerals in some products and fat in some others. | Eat foods containing fat sparingly and look out for the low-fat alternatives. Foods containing sugar should not be eaten too often, as they can contribute to tooth decay. | Some foods containing fat will be eaten every day, but should be kept to small amounts, for example, margarine and butter, other spreading fats (including low-fat spreads), cooking oils, oil-based salad dressings and mayonnaise. Foods contaning fat such as cakes, biscuits, pastries and ice cream should be limited and low-fat alternatives chosaen where available. All foods containing sugar should be eaten mainly at mealtimes to reduce the risk of tooth decay. |

* 'Fibre' is more properly known as non-starch polysaccharides (NSP)

Source – Health Education Authority

# Nutrient needs

Different people have different nutrient needs, depending on their age, life-style, sex, activities, stage of life (adolescence, pregnancy, lactation etc.). The Committee on Nutritional Aspects of Food Policy (COMA) report in 1991 detailed the ranges of energy and nutrient intakes needed by different people each day. These are called **dietary reference values (DRV)**. The DRVs are guidelines for groups of people, not individuals. For most nutrients the values are called **reference nutrient intakes (RNI)**. This is the amount of the nutrient which will meet the needs of almost everyone in that group. The RNIs have been calculated for:
- protein
- nine vitamins
- eleven minerals.

The values which have been calculated for energy and nutrient requirements for different groups of people are called **estimated average requirements (EAR)**. The six main tables on this page and on the page opposite show the dietary reference values for children (7–10 years), adolescents (11–14 years and 15–18 years) and for adults (19–50 years, 51–59 years and over 75).

COMA also suggested general guidelines about where the energy in our diet should come from. These are shown in the small table below.

| Nutrient | Energy in the diet (%) |
|---|---|
| fats (saturated and unsaturated) | 30–35 |
| protein | 15 |
| carbohydrates – sugar | 11 |
| – starches | 39 |

**Dietary Reference Values for adolescents (11–14 years)**

| | Male | Female |
|---|---|---|
| Energy (MJ/day) (EAR) | 9.27 | 7.72 |
| protein (g/day) | 42.1 | 41.2 |
| thiamin (mg/day) | 0.9 | 0.7 |
| riboflavin (mg/day) | 1.2 | 1.1 |
| niacin (mg/day) | 15.0 | 12.0 |
| folate ($\mu$g/day) | 200.0 | 200.0 |
| vitamin $B_{12}$ ($\mu$g/day) | 1.2 | 1.2 |
| vitamin C (mg/day) | 35.0 | 35.0 |
| vitamin A ($\mu$g/day) | 600.0 | 600.0 |
| vitamin D ($\mu$g/day) | no dietary value given | no dietary value given |
| calcium (mg/day | 1000.0 | 800.0 |
| sodium (mg/day) | 1600.0 | 1600.0 |
| iron (mg/day) | 11.3 | 14.8 |

**Dietary Reference Values for children (7–10 years)**

| | Male | Female |
|---|---|---|
| Energy (MJ/day) (EAR) | 8.24 | 7.28 |
| protein (g/day) | 28.3 | 28.3 |
| thiamin (mg/day) | 0.7 | 0.7 |
| riboflavin (mg/day) | 1.0 | 1.0 |
| niacin (mg/day) | 12.0 | 12.0 |
| folate ($\mu$g/day) | 150.0 | 150.0 |
| vitamin $B_{12}$ ($\mu$g/day) | 1.0 | 1.0 |
| vitamin C (mg/day) | 30.0 | 30.0 |
| vitamin A ($\mu$g/day) | 500.0 | 500.0 |
| vitamin D ($\mu$g/day) | no dietary value given | no dietary value given |
| calcium (mg/day) | 550.0 | 550.0 |
| sodium (mg/day) | 1200.0 | 1200.0 |
| iron (mg/day) | 8.7 | 8.7 |

**Dietary Reference Values for adolescents (15–18 years)**

| | Male | Female |
|---|---|---|
| Energy (MJ/day) (EAR) | 11.51 | 8.83 |
| protein (g/day) | 55.2 | 45.0 |
| thiamin (mg/day) | 1.1 | 0.8 |
| riboflavin (mg/day) | 1.3 | 1.1 |
| niacin (mg/day) | 18.0 | 14.0 |
| folate ($\mu$g/day) | 200.0 | 200.0 |
| vitamin $B_{12}$ ($\mu$g/day) | 1.5 | 1.5 |
| vitamin C (mg/day) | 40.0 | 40.0 |
| vitamin A ($\mu$g/day) | 700.0 | 600.0 |
| vitamin D ($\mu$g/day) | no dietary value given | no dietary value given |
| calcium (mg/day) | 1000.0 | 800.0 |
| sodium (mg/day) | 1600.0 | 1600.0 |
| iron (mg/day) | 11.3 | 14.8 |

## Dietary Reference Values for adults (19–50 years)

|  | Male | Female |
|---|---|---|
| Energy (MJ/day) (EAR) | 10.6 | 8.1 |
| protein (g/day) | 55.5 | 45.0 |
| thiamin (mg/day) | 1.0 | 0.8 |
| riboflavin (mg/day) | 1.3 | 1.1 |
| niacin (mg/day) | 17.0 | 13.0 |
| folate (μg/day) | 200.0 | 200.0 |
| vitamin B$_{12}$ (μg/day) | 1.5 | 1.5 |
| vitamin C (mg/day) | 40.0 | 40.0 |
| vitamin A (μg/day) | 700.0 | 600.0 |
| vitamin D (μg/day) | no dietary value given | no dietary value given |
| calcium (mg/day) | 700.0 | 700.0 |
| sodium (mg/day) | 1600.0 | 1600.0 |
| iron (mg/day) | 8.7 | 14.8 |

## Dietary Reference Values for adults (75+ years)

|  | Male | Female |
|---|---|---|
| Energy (MJ/day) (EAR) | 8.77 | 7.61 |
| protein (g/day)† | 53.3 | 46.5 |
| thiamin (mg/day) | 0.9 | 0.8 |
| riboflavin (mg/day) | 1.3 | 1.1 |
| niacin (mg/day)† | 16.0 | 12.0 |
| folate (μg/day) | 200.0 | 200.0 |
| vitamin B$_{12}$ (μg/day) | 1.5 | 1.5 |
| vitamin C (mg/day) | 40.0 | 40.0 |
| vitamin A (μg/day) | 700.0 | 600.0 |
| vitamin D (μg/day) | 10.0 | 10.0 |
| calcium (mg/day | 700.0 | 700.0 |
| sodium (mg/day) | 1600.0 | 1600.0 |
| iron (mg/day) | 8.7 | 8.7 |

Source – Department of Health, *Dietary Reference Values for Food Energy and Nutrients for the United Kingdom*

## Dietary Reference Values for adults (51–59 years)

|  | Male | Female |
|---|---|---|
| Energy (MJ/day) (EAR) | 10.60 | 8.00 |
| protein (g/day) | 53.3 | 46.5 |
| thiamin (mg/day) | 0.9 | 0.8 |
| riboflavin (mg/day) | 1.3 | 1.1 |
| niacin (mg/day) | 16.0 | 12.0 |
| folate (μg/day) | 200.0 | 200.0 |
| vitamin B$_{12}$ (μg/day) | 1.5 | 1.5 |
| vitamin C (mg/day) | 40.0 | 40.0 |
| vitamin A (μg/day) | 700.0 | 600.0 |
| vitamin D (μg/day) | no dietary value given | no dietary value given |
| calcium (mg/day) | 700.0 | 700.0 |
| sodium (mg/day) | 1600.0 | 1600.0 |
| iron (mg/day) | 8.7 | 8.7 |

## Tasks

3 Use the ingredients list below – from a pack of pasta with sauce – to identify the sources of fat, protein and carbohydrates.

4 What is the value to the consumer of the information in the 'blue flash' panel?

### INGREDIENTS

PASTA (DURUM WHEAT SEMOLINA, WHOLE EGG); ASPARAGUS, RICOTTA FULL-FAT WHEY CHEESE, BREADCRUMBS, POTATO FLAKE (WITH PRESERVATIVE: SULPHUR DIOXIDE), PARMESAN MEDIUM-FAT HARD CHEESE, SALT, OLIVE OIL, PARSLEY, GARLIC.

### NUTRITION INFORMATION

TYPICAL VALUES (COOKED AS PER INSTRUCTIONS) PER 100 g (3.5 oz):
**ENERGY** 143 kcal, 603 KJ., **PROTEIN** 6.0 g, **CARBOHYDRATE** 23.4 g OF WHICH SUGARS 0.2 g, STARCH 22.7 g, **FAT** 2.8 g OF WHICH SATURATES 1.3 g,. MONO-UNSATURATES 1.2 g, POLYUNSATURATES 0.3 g, **FIBRE** 2.1 g, **SODIUM** 0.1 g
TYPICAL VALUES (COOKED AS PER INSTRUCTIONS) PER $\frac{1}{2}$ PACK:
**ENERGY** 294 kcal, 1241 KJ., **PROTEIN** 12.3 g, **CARBOHYDRATE** 48.3 g OF WHICH SUGARS 0.4 g, STARCH 46.8 g, **FAT** 5.7g OF WHICH SATURATES 2.7 g, MONO-UNSATURATES 2.5 g POLYUNSATURATES 0.5 g, **FIBRE** 4.3 g, **SODIUM** 0.2 g.

| PER 1/2 PACK | 294 CALORIES | 5.7 g FAT |
|---|---|---|

## Task

2 Compare the energy needs of 15–18 year olds with those of 51–59 year olds. Why do they differ?

Ingredients and nutrition information from a pack of pasta with sauce

# Translating the COMA guidelines into foods

The suggested guidelines which COMA made refer to where, and in what percentage, energy in the diet should be provided, but how can this be translated into foods?

## Fats

The chemical name to remember is **triglyceride**. This is made up of three fatty acids in chains, joined to a molecule of **glycerol.** The diagram below shows a triglyceride.

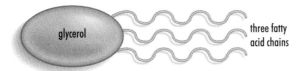

glycerol — three fatty acid chains

■ A triglyceride

Fatty acids consist of a chain of carbon atoms, each of which can link with four other atoms.

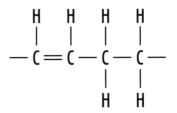

■ Diagram 1: a saturated fatty acid

Notice that in the diagram above:
▶ all the carbon atoms are attached to hydrogen
▶ all the links called **bonds** are single (shown by single lines).
This shows a saturated fatty acid.
   If the required number of other bonds, such as hydrogen, are not available the carbon links back on itself and forms a double bond. Notice in diagram **2** that there is one set of double lines. This shows an **unsaturated fatty acid**. When the chain has only one double bond (as in diagram **2**) it is called a **mono-unsaturated** fatty acid. When there is more than one double bond in a chain it is called a **polyunsaturated** fatty acid.

■ Diagram 2: a mono-unsaturated fatty acid

The relevance of this to the development of food products is that:
▶ fat containing a high proportion of saturated fatty acids (sometimes called **saturates**) are usually solid at room temperature and have high melting points. These are mainly of animal origin e.g. pork, lamb, beef. Lard, butter and cream have a high proportion of saturates. Hard margarines and some fats of vegetable origin such as palm oil and coconut oil also have a high proportion of saturates.
▶ fats containing a high proportion of unsaturated fatty acids (sometimes called **mono-unsaturates** and **polyunsaturates**) are softer or liquid at room temperature because they have lower melting points. Examples of foods with a high proportion of mono-unsaturated fatty acids include olive oil (roughly 70 per cent of its composition is mono-unsaturated), groundnut oil and the oil in fish such as salmon, herring, and mackerel. Examples of food with a high proportion of polyunsaturated fatty acids include oil from sunflower, soya, sesame and safflower seeds. These oils are used to make oils and margarine which are sold as being high in polyunsaturates.

FLORA
Sunflower Spread
HIGH IN ESSENTIAL POLYUNSATURATES
Low in Saturates ⚬ Low in Cholesterol

■ Many spreads are high in polyunsaturates

### TESCO

*Pure*

## SUNFLOWER

# OIL

A LIGHT, ALL - PURPOSE OIL IDEAL
FOR FRYING AND SALAD DRESSINGS
High in Polyunsaturates,
Low in Saturates

500 ml ℮

BEST BEFORE END:
SEE DATE BELOW CAP

■ Sunflower oil is also
high in polyunsatures

The table shows which fats people bought in the period 1992–4. What other information is useful to consumers when they make food choices?

▶ The COMA (Committee on Medical Aspects of Food Policy) report on 'Dietary Reference Values for Food Energy and Nutrients for the United Kingdom' (1991)

▶ 'The Health of the Nation', a Government white paper published in 1992 which contained nutritional and dietary targets to be reached by the year 2005. The targets set out:

- to reduce the average percentage of food energy from saturated fatty acids by at least 35 per cent to eleven per cent
- to reduce the average percentage of food energy from total fat by at least twelve per cent, to no more than 35 per cent
- to reduce the number of men and women aged 16–64 who are very overweight (obese) by one quarter for women and one third for men.

## Consumer choice

| Consumption of fats 1992–4 | | | |
|---|---|---|---|
| | Consumption per person per week | | |
| | 1992 | 1993 | 1994 |
| | grams* | | |
| butter | 41 | 40 | 39 |
| margarine | 79 | 70 | 43 |
| low-fat and dairy spreads | 51 | 52 | 74 |
| vegetable and salad oils (ml) | 49 | 46 | 49 |
| other fats and oils | 25 | 23 | 21 |
| total fats | 245 | 230 | 226 |
| * except where otherwise stated. | | | |

Source: MAFF, *National Food Survey*, 1994

━━ *Tasks* ━━

5 Study the nutritional and dietary targets recommended in 'The Health of the Nation'.

   a Do you think they will be achieved by the bulk of the population by the year 2005?

   b How effective is their achievement now? Is progress being made? If so, by whom?

6 In relation to obesity, it is better not to become overweight in the first place. Write one sentence which could show people how to avoid putting on too much weight.

When designing and making food products it is helpful to remember:

▶ a reduction in fat consumption needs to be accompanied by an increase in consumption of staple foods which are rich in starch and fibre, such as potatoes, rice, pasta, bread, vegetables and fruit

▶ a 'fat audit' of a product or a range of products would identify what reductions in fat and saturated fat there could be whilst making sure the product could be made successfully and also meet consumer expectations.

### What progress is being made?

The table below shows the progress which has been made so far in reducing the percentage of food energy from fats. This information is useful because when developing new products or modifying existing ones it is important to know about changes in demand. The targets set for 2005 and the small reduction in the intake of fats that the table shows suggest that consumers are trying to reduce fat intake, which means that products that take this into account have a better chance of selling well.

| Proportions of household food energy derived from total fat and saturated fatty acids | | | | |
|---|---|---|---|---|
| | Percentage of food energy* | | | 'The Health of the Nation' |
| | 1992 | 1993 | 1994 | target for 2005 |
| Fat | 41.7 | 41.3 | 40.5 | 35.0 |
| of which: saturated fatty acids | 16.3 | 16.1 | 15.7 | 11.0 |
| * excluding soft and alcoholic drinks and confectionery. | | | | |

Source – MAFF, *National Food Survey*, 1994

## Starches and sugars

Other sources of energy in the diet are starches and sugars. These are the products of photosynthesis in plants and are called carbohydrates. Carbohydrates are made up of carbon, hydrogen and oxygen (two parts of hydrogen to one part of oxygen). The simplest carbohydrates are called **monosaccharides**. Glucose, fructose and galactose are included in this group. More complex carbohydrates are called **disaccharides**. These are made up of two monosaccharides joined together. Lactose (the sugar in milk), sucrose (ordinary sugar) and maltose are included in this group. **Polysaccharides** are large units of many monosaccharide units joined together.

Monosaccharides and disaccharides are sugars. Polysaccharides found in plants are starch, polysaccharides found in animals are glycogen.

### How are these facts used in product development?

Sugars fall into two groups. There are those which are naturally present in foods, such as fruit and vegetables, then there is the sugar which is added to foods. Manufacturers add sugar to some sauces, for example tomato sauce, and many people add sugar to drinks and other foods to sweeten them to suit their taste. The sugars which are present naturally in foods are called **intrinsic** sugars. The sugar which is added is called **extrinsic** sugar.

Extrinsic sugars are added to all kinds of products, such as cereals, sauces, soft drinks etc. The term **non-milk extrinsic sugars (NMES)** is used to describe table sugar and the sugar in products such as cakes, fruit juice, honey and biscuits. NMES can contribute to dental decay and also build up reliance on sweetness for flavour and so on.

Non-milk extrinsic sugars are sometimes 'hidden' in products such as canned vegetables, soups and pickles, where you would not normally think that sugar would be present. The label often describes these on the ingredients list as sucrose, dextrose, maltodextrin or glucose.

*Non-starch polysaccharide*

The term for dietary fibre is **non-starch polysaccharide (NSP)**. Fibre is a carbohydrate which provides little energy. It does, however, help to lower blood cholesterol which, in turn, helps to reduce the risk of coronary heart disease (CHD). This type of fibre is found in oats and is a **soluble** fibre. Another type of fibre found particularly in wheat bran is **insoluble**. It makes food pass through the body quickly and helps to reduce the incidence of constipation and other bowel disorders. For this reason there is a dietary guideline for the consumption of fibre or NSP. The DRV recommended is 12–24 g per day, with an average daily intake of 18 g recommended for adults. Children should eat less than the 18 g and those under two years should not be given foods rich in NSP at the expense of foods which supply energy.

A dietary recommendation by COMA is that the intake of NSP (fibre) should be increased for the majority of the population. Figures in 1991 showed that the average intake was about twelve grams per day but that some people's intake was as low as five grams per day.

One of the benefits of increasing fibre intake is that most food sources which are high in fibre are also low in fat. Examples include lentils, beans, peas, nuts, fruit and vegetables (especially when the skin is left on) and wholemeal products such as pasta and brown rice. Another benefit is that fibre-rich foods are often very filling but are relatively low in the energy they provide, which makes them particularly useful in the development of nutritious products for the 'weight control' and 'low-fat' markets.

*Reminders about* NSP

▶ There are two types of fibre – soluble and insoluble.
▶ Soluble fibre may help to lower blood cholesterol (which is thought to be a factor in the risk of coronary heart disease).
▶ Oats contain soluble fibre.
▶ Insoluble fibre increases the speed at which food passes through the body (called **transit time**).
▶ Wheat bran contains insoluble fibre.

## Salt

Another dietary guideline concerns salt (**sodium chloride**). At the moment sodium intake comes from:
▶ table salt (15–20 per cent)
▶ salt used during food processing (60–70 per cent)
▶ naturally occurring sodium in some foods (roughly 15 per cent).

The recommendation is to reduce the intake of sodium by roughly a third. This recommendation is important in development of food products and should be considered by food technologists so that reductions are made. Ways to reduce salt intake include:
▶ using less in preparation and cooking, and flavouring food by adding other ingredients such as herbs and spices
▶ not adding salt to food on the plate
▶ using low sodium salt which has about a third of the sodium in 'regular' salt, (the other two-thirds are potassium chloride).

*Some facts and figures*

At the moment salt intake is about nine grams per day. Experts say this is much too high. They say the amount should drop to six grams per day.

◇

## Tasks

7 Take-away and fast-food products are popular with most young people. These foods are often low in fibre and high in fat. Bearing in mind the targets set for 2005, list six pieces of advice which will help young people establish good dietary habits.

8 Design and make a low-fat, high-fibre 'burger in a bun' product.

# The functional properties of food

*L*ook at the above illustration. All of the food products shown in this illustration are based on fat, flour and liquid, yet they are very different in appearance, texture and taste.

## How can these differences be produced?

In industrial and domestic food processing, knowledge of how to use the qualities which a food possesses is applied to produce the variety of products demanded by consumers.

## What knowledge is required?

What happens to food during processing depends on the physical and chemical nature of food (the qualities which a food possesses). These qualities are called **properties**. Because food technologists use these properties to make products successful, the properties are described as **functional properties**.

The functional properties are used to bring about the changes required to make a successful product which people will buy. Processing can alter the flavour, appearance, texture, aroma, colour and nutritional value of food. Food technologists need to apply their knowledge of the functional properties of food to bring about these alterations or changes.

## Task

1 a Think of some food products which you enjoy eating and make a list of these products.

b Describe the colour, taste, texture, appearance, and aroma of each.

c Choose one of the characteristics from **b**. Explain why that characteristic makes one of the products you have listed popular with you i.e. why do you like it?

## How do changes to food happen?

Factors that cause changes to food include:
▸ the surroundings (environmental factors) such as heat, cold, light, air
▸ the combination and proportion of foods as in a recipe for a particular product e.g. a pastry or a sugar syrup
▸ the mechanical forces used in mixing e.g. beating, whisking, stirring
▸ how **acidic** or **alkaline** the food or combinations of ingredients are. This is called the pH of food.

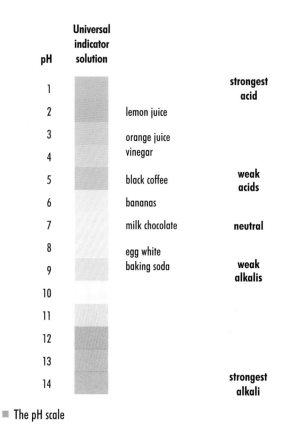

■ The pH scale

# What is pH?

pH is measured on a scale of 1 to 14. The diagram above shows the pH scale.
Notice that:
▶ neutral has a measurement of 7 and is neither acidic nor alkaline
▶ between 7 and 1 a solution or food becomes more acidic
▶ between 7 and 14 a solution or food becomes more alkaline.

# Why is a knowledge of pH useful?

If the pH value of a food is low, the acidity or sour taste will be very noticeable. This could mean that a product containing this food may be too sour for most consumers and may not sell very well. An example of this might be a lemon pudding where the amount of lemon juice in the recipe is too high to produce the sweet-sour flavour most consumers like.

Yoghurt is another example where the pH value is critical to the product's success. It is made from milk which has a pH of between 6.4 and 6.7. Most yoghurts on the market have a pH between 4.2 and 4.3 which is the level of acidity that has been found to ensure that a successful product results and one which is acceptable to consumers (i.e. not too sour for most people's tastes). Therefore, during manufacture the acidity of the milk must be raised.

Sour milk has a lower pH (higher acidity) than fresh milk as a result of bacteria which break down the sugar in milk (lactose) to an acid substance, called **lactic acid**. When the pH is lowered to around 5.2 the milk curdles. Curdling happens because one of the major proteins in milk, **casein** separates out from the liquid at the acidic level around 5.2.

During the manufacture of yoghurt, bacteria are added to the milk. This causes lactic acid to be produced, which lowers the pH and allows a thicker product with a distinctive flavour to develop.

If a mixture is very alkaline, that is has a high pH, an unpleasant bitter flavour results. This is why if bicarbonate of soda (which has a high pH) is included in a recipe, an acid medium is also included. Two examples are sour milk and cream of tartar (made from tartaric acid). The acid medium lowers the pH and produces a more acceptable flavour.

The following table gives the pH values for a selection of foods.

| pH of selected foods | | | |
|---|---|---|---|
| **Food** | **pH** | **Food** | **pH** |
| Apple juice | 3.8 | Potatoes | 6.1 |
| Grapefruit | 3.0–3.3 | Cocoa | 5.2–6.0 |
| Lemon | 2.2–2.4 | Tomatoes | 4.1–4.4 |
| Vinegar | 2.4–3.4 | White bread | 5.0–6.0 |
| Chocolate | 6.0–7.8 | Bananas | 5.6 |
| Egg white | 7.6–9.7 | Carrots | 4.9–5.2 |
| Milk | 6.4–6.7 | | |

# Solutions

The liquid in which things dissolve is called a **solvent**. The material which dissolves is called a **solute**. Sugar and salt are solutes when they are dissolved in a liquid. A solute dissolved in a solvent makes a **solution**. The following table gives some examples.

| Solution | Solute | Solvent |
|---|---|---|
| syrup | sugar | water |
| fizzy drink | gas (carbon dioxide) | flavoured water |
| brine | salt | water |

Where small amounts of solute are used the solution is **diluted**. Where relatively high amounts of solute are used the solution is **concentrated**.

## What other properties are important?

The **specific gravity** of a material is its *weight compared with the weight of an equal volume of water at a given temperature*. This information is useful when developing new products. For example, the specific gravity of milk would be used in the development of a new product based on milk:

▶ as the fat content of milk increases the specific gravity decreases; this means that 'full-fat' milk has a low specific gravity

▶ as the 'non-fat' solids of milk increase the specific gravity increases.

## How is this information used?

A food technologist will test the specific gravity of a material to find out if it meets the specification for the development of a new product. For example, in yoghurt production, the level of non-fat solids in the product must be high so that the product will set. Specific gravity also indicates the amount of air in a mixture – in whisked egg white and creamed fat and sugar the more air in the mixture the lower the specific gravity.

## Melting point

The melting point is the temperature at which a material changes *from* a solid *to* a liquid. When working with food, the temperature at which a material softens is often important during processing, for example successful creaming of fat and sugar for a cake is achieved when the fat is soft, not liquid.

## Freezing point

The freezing point is the temperature at which a material changes *from* a liquid *to* a solid. The point at which this happens varies according to the material. The freezing point of a salt solution is lower than that of water, and a sugar solution freezes at a higher temperature than a salt solution. The freezing point of water is 0°C. Food technologists use this information when developing systems to freeze vegetables or to make ice cream, for example.

## Boiling point

Every liquid has its own characteristic boiling point. However, the boiling point of a liquid can be affected by atmospheric pressure and what is in the solution.

▶ **Atmospheric pressure**
**Standard atmospheric pressure** is 14.7 lb per square inch. At this pressure plain (pure) water boils at 100°C. When atmospheric pressure is lower than standard atmospheric pressure, water boils at a temperature lower than 100°C (this occurs on a mountain top where the pressure is lower than at sea level). When it is higher than standard atmospheric pressure, water boils at a higher temperature than 100°C. Pressure cookers reduce cooking times because of this. The table below shows the temperatures which apply at different pressure settings on a pressure cooker.

| Setting | Pressure *above* atmospheric pressure | | Temperature |
|---|---|---|---|
| | (lb per square inch) | (kg per cm²) | |
| Atmospheric | 0 | 0 | 100 |
| Low | 5 | 0.35 | 108 |
| Medium | 10 | 0.70 | 115 |
| High | 15 | 1.05 | 121 |

## ▬ *Task* ▬

2  Carry out a test to prove that pressure cookers reduce cooking times.

Prepare two samples of potato each weighing 200 g and cut into six even sized pieces. Boil one sample in an ordinary saucepan in salted water. Record the time it takes to cook, in a table like the one below.

Cook the other sample in a pressure cooker for the time stated in the instruction booklet. Record the time it takes to cook. Compare your results.

| Time taken | Result |
|---|---|
| Ordinary saucepan | |
| Pressure cooker | |

The information you have gathered could be useful in design-and-make tasks which require different types of cooking instructions for vegetables.

### ▶ **What is in the solution**

A sugar syrup solution boils at a higher temperature than 100°C. The more sugar (solute) there is to water (solvent) in the solution the higher the temperature at which it boils. This fact is used by the food technologist when making different products with sugar solutions. Understanding the relationship between sugar content and boiling point is critical for success. Marmalade, for example, has a 68 per cent concentration of sugar and boils at around 105°C, whereas fudge has an 82 per cent concentration of sugar and boils at around 115°C.

When a sugar solution boils, water vapour is driven off and the concentration of the solution increases, which raises the boiling point of the solution (see table).

| The relationship between sugar content and boiling point | | | | | |
|---|---|---|---|---|---|
| Sugar (%) | 40 | 50 | 60 | 70 | 80 | 90 |
| Boiling point (°C) | 101.5 | 102.5 | 103.0 | 106.5 | 112.0 | 130.0 |

■ Information about sugar content and boiling point is used when new jams and jellies are being developed

This information is used when products such as jams and jellies are being developed. A sugar boiling thermometer can be used to measure the percentage of sugar in a product accurately.

*Important points to remember*

▶ The higher the temperature the greater the amount of sugar which can be dissolved.
▶ The amount of solute dissolved in a solvent is called the **concentration** of a solution.
▶ A **saturated solution** is made when no more solute will dissolve in a solvent. This means that the maximum amount of sugar for that degree of concentration in a sugared solution has been dissolved.
▶ **Crystals** form when the solution cools down.
▶ Invert sugar (see pages 64–5) prevents large crystals forming.
▶ The solution must not be beaten until it has cooled down, otherwise large crystals will form and the product will fail. For example, large crystals would produce a lumpy consistency in the softened fondant used to make the filling for some after-dinner mints.

# Other factors which bring about changes in food

Many foods have properties which allow them to be changed into other forms. These changes are used quite a lot in the development of food products. It is important to understand how to bring about and use these changes in foods, to carry out successful design-and-make tasks.

When a change in food results from a physical factor the change is **not permanent**. An example of this is when water boils and steam is produced. On cooling the steam changes back to water. Another example of a change which is not permanent is chocolate – on heating it melts and on cooling it becomes solid again. Changes like these are **reversible**.

■ A reversible change

Other changes can take place in food that are permanent, or **irreversible**. An example of this is when flour is mixed with a liquid and a paste is formed. This is a simple example of a **permanent** change.

## Crystallization

The control of crystallization is an important aspect of food processing. The chemical name for sugar is sucrose. When a solution of sucrose is boiled a chemical change takes place. The sucrose changes into two other types of sugar, glucose and fructose. These are known as **invert** sugars and the process of splitting up is called **inversion**. During inversion water is incorporated. This is called **hydrolysis**.

Food technologists use this information when making confectionery, jams and similar products. Including sufficient invert sugar in the product prevents large sugar crystals forming. If too little invert sugar is present in a product sucrose will slowly crystallize out during storage. It is important to know this because if, for example, the sugar crystallizes and makes a jam 'gritty' it will not meet consumers' expectations and will not sell well. Glucose and fructose are prepared commercially for use in the manufacture of some jams and marmalades and sweets such as fondants, because they do not crystallize easily.

## — Tasks

3 a Investigate how one ingredient can affect another.
  ▶ Mix small amounts of oil and vinegar together.
  ▶ Mix milk and lemon juice.
 b Record what happens to each ingredient. You could use a copy of the table below.
 c Decide whether the change that has taken place is reversible or irreversible.

4 a Try these simple experiments.
  ▶ Make up a commercial jelly.
  ▶ Make up a sachet of instant soup.
 b Observe what happens in each case. Record the changes in a table like the one below.
 c Are the changes reversible or irreversible?

| Ingredients used | How? | What happened? | Is the change reversible? | How can you tell? |
| --- | --- | --- | --- | --- |
|  |  |  |  |  |
|  |  |  |  |  |

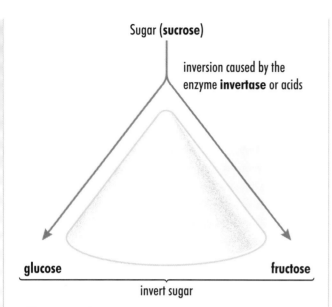

**Sugar (sucrose)**

inversion caused by the enzyme **invertase** or acids

**glucose**

**fructose**

invert sugar

■ The inversion of sucrose

*How else is this information used?*

So that a product will store well, or have a long shelf life, the manufacturer sometimes adds other ingredients to ensure that crystallization will not take place before the expiry of storage time claimed for that product. These ingredients can help to prevent or delay crystallization. Cream, milk, chocolate, starch and gelatin are examples of ingredients which can be used in this way.

## Fermentation

It is important for food technologists to understand fermentation, which also causes changes to take place in food. For example, naturally occurring sugars in fruits are easily fermented by bacteria and yeasts. One of the harmful effects of this is the spoilage of fruits and vegetables. Beneficial effects of fermentation are used in the production of bread and the manufacture of alcoholic drinks. A by-product of fermentation is carbon dioxide, which is used to produce the 'fizz' in some popular drinks.

## Traditional STYLE

# Ginger Beer

CONCENTRATE MAKES 7.5 LITRES

■ Concentrate can be used to make fizzy drinks at home

— *Task* ▬▬

5 There is a high rate of consumption of sweets of all kinds in the UK.
  a Investigate:
   (i) how much money is spent on sweets and chocolate in one day at your local supermarket or shop
   (ii) the most popular sweets and chocolate products.
  b Imagine you are a designer for a large confectionery manufacturer. Use the results of your investigation to suggest two products (one a sweet, one a chocolate product) which would be worth developing.

— *Task* ▬▬

6 a Investigate how home-made fizzy drinks can be made using tap water and a concentrate such as the one shown above.
  b What are the advantages of being able to make your own fizzy drinks?
  c Is this a good by-product of the fermentation process?
  d If you have access to a Sodastream or similar piece of equipment, try it out by making up one or two different flavours.

# What other changes help to produce palatable food?

One very important way is concerned with the texture and consistency of foods. Recipes call for different qualities to be produced during product development. These qualities can determine whether a product meets the criteria for its development and whether it fits consumers' expectations of the product e.g. the mouth feel when eaten must be what the consumer finds palatable and appetizing.

## Starch

The way starch behaves when it is processed plays an important part in the texture and consistency of food products. Starch does not dissolve in cold water but when the mixture is heated the water penetrates (gets inside) the starch granules and they swell and soften. When this happens the mixture changes from being fluid (thin and watery) and becomes thicker. This usually takes place at temperatures of 79–93 °C. The more starch there is in proportion to the liquid in the mixture, the thicker the mixture becomes. This is called **gelatinization**. In food technology, how thick the mixture becomes is called its **viscosity**.

Gelatinization allows a mixture to form a gel. This usually happens when the mixture cools down and gelling or setting takes place.

*How is this knowledge used?*

Food technologists need to work out the proportions of different foods in a mixture to ensure the product meets the specification for consistency and texture. For example, a sauce used to coat vegetables must be thick enough to provide an even coating. If it is too thick it will not give a smooth consistency, or if it is too thin it will simply run off the vegetables.

Starches used in food preparation include wheat starch (flour), corn starch (cornflour), rice and tapioca. Food technologists choose the one which will give the required results for a particular product. For example, rice is used with milk to make a thickened milk pudding and many sauces are thickened with flour.

■ The lemon filling in lemon meringue pie is thickened by the gelatinization of starch and the coagulation of egg protein

■ The gel created in making a blancmange allows the cold mixture to hold its shape

*Other facts which food technologists must use*

The addition of the following foods affects texture and consistency.

▶ **Sugar** – If too much sugar is added to a starch and liquid mixture gelling will not take place and a thin, runny mixture will be produced.

▶ **Acid** e.g. lemon juice – If an acid is cooked with starch and liquid the thickening quality of the starch is reduced. Lemon juice or any other acidic ingredients must be added to the mixture after cooking and thickening has taken place.

*More facts*

▶ Stirring and beating a sauce mixture thickened with starch helps to break down the starch granules and produce a shiny smooth sauce.

▶ When a starch gel is kept for some time liquid begins to appear. This is sometimes described as weeping or **syneresis**. The starch in the mixture has become less soluble during storage and begins to go back to its pre-gelatinized form. This is called **retrogradation** of starch. In food manufacture modified starches are used to prevent this happening.

**Task**

7 a Find a recipe for a dish which includes making a thickened mixture using starch and a liquid. Some examples are blancmange, cheese sauce to coat vegetables or lasagne, or a stir-fry.

b Make up the recipe according to the instructions.

c Record the changes which happen to the sauce during preparation and cooking.

d Allow the dish to cool. (Remember to cool it quickly and then refrigerate it.)

e Describe the consistency of the sauce on cooling.

f Find a similar commercial product. Look at the ingredients label. Find out what has been used to thicken the product.

# Gelatin and pectin

Some products have to be set, to meet the expectations of the consumer. Cold desserts, jellies and jams are some examples. Gelatin and pectin are used to set products, both commercially and in domestic cooking.

## Gelatin

Gelatin is a protein which dissolves in a hot liquid. On cooling, the gelatin solution thickens, gels and can hold its shape. The solution will set at room temperature given time but gelling is quicker if the mixture is put in a refrigerator. Gelatin is used to set cold desserts such as jellies.

### Other facts about gelatin

▶ Occasional stirring during setting prevents lumps forming.
▶ Beating during setting produces a light and spongy mixture.
▶ Cream, egg whites and flavouring can be added to increase the range of products, for example soufflés, mousses.

■ Gelatin is used to set jellies into interesting shapes

■ This strawberry mousse contains cream and egg whites as well as gelatin

▶ Fresh pineapple destroys the gelling ability of gelatin. Fresh pineapple must be boiled for about two minutes before use with gelatin if a set is needed.
▶ The ratio of gelatin to liquid used is critical. Mixtures with a high acid content need a higher ratio of gelatin to water than other mixtures. Examples include making a tomato or lemon mixture.

## Pectin

Fruit can be preserved in the form of jams and jellies. Fruits contain pectin which make the mixture gel or set. In jam-making, sugar, water and fruit are boiled and pectin is released from the fruit. When the mixture cools a set gel is formed.

For gelling to happen the mixture must be fairly acid (pH approximately 3.2). Lemon juice or citric acid can be added to lower the pH. Plums and apples contain large amounts of pectin, as do strawberries and blackberries. When jam is made commercially, pectin and citric acid (from apples or citrus fruits) are always used to make sure the product is successful.

■ These products are 'set' using pectin

The pH must be carefully controlled to get the right level of acidity. In the large-scale manufacture of jam, a **buffering agent** such as **calcium citrate** (**E333**) might be used to control the acidity level. In reduced-sugar jams the gel must be produced by an alternative ingredient. Chemically modified pectins are used in these products to produce a gel, to make sure the jam sets. The gels produced in this way are kept firm or **stabilized** with another added ingredient, which could be a gum.

## Protein

Protein also plays a part in the development of consistency and texture. The best example is egg protein. Eggs are used to thicken products such as custards. This is how it happens. When eggs are heated they change from a fluid to a more solid state. When this happens a gel is formed. Egg white thickens or sets between 62°C and 70°C. The yolk thickens between 65°C and 70°C. This thickening is called **coagulation**. When eggs are beaten into a liquid and then heated, coagulation makes the mixture thicken. An example of this is when an egg custard is made.

*Other facts*

When making mixtures with eggs controlling the temperature is critical.
▶ The firmness of a custard is increased when the proportion of egg to liquid is increased.
▶ The addition of sugar raises the temperature at which coagulation takes place.
▶ Heating beyond the point at which coagulation takes place increases the set and can produce a tough product which shrinks and as a result weeps because the liquid is squeezed out.

=== *Task* ===

8 a  Make a baked custard using the following recipe.

> ### Ingredients:
> 1 egg, 200 ml milk, 10 g sugar, pinch of nutmeg
>
> ### Method:
> 1  Beat together the egg, milk and sugar.
> 2  Strain into a small ovenproof dish (e.g. 300 ml pie dish).
> 3  Sprinkle nutmeg on top.
> 4  Place the dish in a baking tin. Put cold water in the tin to come three-quarters of the way up the dish.
> 5  Bake for approximately 20 minutes at 160°C (or until the custard is set).

Comment upon the consistency of the finished product.
b  Compare your custard with a similar commercial 'ready-to-eat' product. Use the following headings for your comparison.
  ▶ Texture and consistency
  ▶ Flavour
  ▶ Ingredients used.

## Colloids, emulsions and emulsifiers

A **colloid** has a gelatinous consistency and is made when one substance is distributed or dispersed (scattered) in another. An example is the gel made when starch and a liquid are heated.

An **emulsion** is a colloid in which fine drops or particles of one liquid are dispersed throughout another liquid with which it cannot mix evenly. There are two kinds of emulsion. The first is **water in oil** and the second is **oil in water**. Mayonnaise, cream and milk are fat (oil) in water emulsions. Butter and margarine are water in oil emulsions.

Emulsions do not form easily because the two substances from which they are made are immiscible (i.e. they do not mix unless made to do so). In food preparation, a mechanical force such as beating is used to achieve a successful mix. Beating increases the surface area of each substance and a smooth product results.

=== *Task* ===

9 a  Find a recipe for making mayonnaise.
   b  What care points are stressed in the method? For example, it may say that small amounts of oil are to be added each time.
   c  What else is added to the oil and vinegar?
   d  Are eggs and mustard mentioned?

### Why add eggs?

Eggs are included in mayonnaise because they prevent the oil and vinegar from separating. Mustard helps to do this too. In this case the egg is acting as an **emulsifier**. Emulsifiers are important in the development of products such as mayonnaise, and margarine. When margarine is heated, the emulsifier delays the separation of fat and water and reduces the risk of 'spitting'. In the case of mayonnaise a substance called **lecithin** in the egg yolk is the emulsifier.

A 'failed' mayonnaise (i.e. one where the oil and vinegar have separated) can be made successful if it is added, drop by drop, to an egg yolk and beaten well. Lecithin is a very efficient emulsifier and is used commercially in many products including chocolate, bread, fats and margarines.

INGREDIENTS: VEGETABLE OIL, WATER, EGG & EGG YOLK, SPIRIT VINEGAR, SALT, SUGAR, LEMON JUICE, MUSTARD EXTRACT, SPICES, ANTIOXIDANT (BHA).

■ Notice the use of egg yolk (lecithin) as an emulsifier in this mayonnaise

## Stabilizers

Stabilizers are used to keep the emulsion stable. The finer or smaller the particles within the emulsion are, the less likely it is to separate but some separation nearly always happens over time. The use of a stabilizer prevents this.

Starch and egg white are the two most commonly used stabilizers. The starch forms a gel which makes it more difficult for the two substances to separate. Egg white has a similar effect. **Modified starches** are widely used commercially to stabilize emulsions. In some commercially produced mayonnaise the stabilizers alginate (E405) and xanthan gum (E415) are used.

| INGREDIENTS |
| --- |
| SUGAR, WHOLE EGG, WHEATFLOUR, CURRANTS, SULTANAS, HYDROGENATED VEGETABLE OIL, GLYCERINE, GLUCOSE SYRUP, BUTTER, MALT EXTRACT, SOYA FLOUR, CORNFLOUR, RAISING AGENTS: DISODIUM DIHYDROGEN DIPHOSPHATE, SODIUM BICARBONATE; MIXED SPICES, MOLASSES, SALT, STABILIZER: XANTHAN GUM; PERSERVATIVE: POTASSIUM SORBATE; EMULSIFIER: POLYSORBATE 60. |

■ The ingredients for cake slices containing the stabilizer xanthan gum

## Foams

A foam is also a colloid and is similar to an emulsion, but it is a gas which is dispersed within the other substance. The gas is usually air or carbon dioxide. Examples include:

▶ **meringues** – foams where whisking or beating has broken down the surface tension and air has been added. The egg white protein, **albumin**, changes its nature (this is **denaturation**) and stretches to take in the air. Too much beating over stretches the protein and the foam collapses and disappears. When this happens the meringue becomes very thin and sticky.

▶ **bread** – in this example, carbon dioxide is produced and is trapped by the gluten in the dough. The foam is produced within the gluten.

▶ **ice cream** – when ice cream is made, air is beaten into the frozen mixture and a foam is produced. This makes the ice cream light and soft with a smooth texture.

## Changes affecting the colour and appearance of food

Colour and appearance are qualities which can affect the consumers' decision to accept or reject food. Making products attractive and the right colour are important aspects of development. Knowledge of what causes colour changes in food must be applied when designing and making food products. The changes which take place are called **browning**. There are four causes of browning.

1 **Non-enzymatic browning** happens when a carbohydrate such as simple sugar reacts with a protein. This produces a full flavour, a good aroma and a brown colour in the product. This is a beneficial change which makes the product more appetizing. This type of browning is sometimes called **Maillard browning** after the Frenchman who discovered it. The outside of meat browns in this way during cooking.

2 **Caramelization** happens when sugar is heated to a temperature above its melting point. Very simply, when sugar is heated at a high temperature for some time it turns brown and has a pleasant toffee-like flavour. However, if heated for too long it becomes very black in appearance and bitter in flavour. Sugar toppings on cakes and pastries can be caramelized to give an attractive appearance and good flavour. Caramel made in this way can be added to custards, ice creams and mousses, etc.

3 **Enzymic browning**, sometimes called **oxidative browning**, occurs when fruits such as apples, bananas and pears are peeled and cut into pieces. Substances in the fruit react with oxygen in the air and produce browning which is unattractive to the consumer. There are

ways of preventing this, which include heating the fruit (as when they are added to a hot syrup for fruit salad), adding acid such as lemon juice, reducing the surface area which limits the exposure to the air (e.g. making larger slice, or leaving the peel on), and blanching.

4 **Dextrinization** occurs when starch is changed to dextrin during cooking. Examples of this include bread and cakes.

■ How did these foods become brown?

■ How did this browning happen? Is it attractive?

71

Raw materials of food are processed to make sure they are edible, can be prepared and cooked and can be preserved so that they are fit to eat when they reach the consumer. The processing of raw materials is called **primary processing**. The two sources of raw materials are:
▶ animals e.g. poultry, fish, cattle, pigs and sheep
▶ crops or plants e.g. vegetables, fruits and cereals.

These sources provide raw materials which are changed into the ingredients used in food processing. Some of the raw materials are discussed below.

## Cereals

During primary processing the grains of cereals are milled to produce flour. When wheat is milled basically two types of flour are made:
▶ white flour is made when only the endosperm is milled (about 70 per cent extraction).
▶ wholemeal flour is made when all parts of the grain are milled (called 100 per cent extraction).

Other types of flour can be produced by adding other materials such as milled wheat and rye or malt extract. This flour is usually described as granary flour.

Flour can also be described by **strength**. This refers to the type of wheat, for example hard wheat from which the flour is milled. Recipes for bread usually state that strong flour should be used. Strong flour is made from hard wheat – a wheat with a high protein content. Strength refers to the protein content of the wheat. The proteins in flour **gliaden** and **glutenin** become gluten when mixed with a liquid.

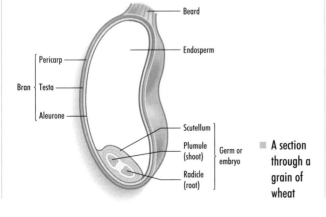

Beard
Endosperm
Pericarp
Bran { Testa
Aleurone
Scutellum
Plumule (shoot)
Germ or embryo
Radicle (root)

■ A section through a grain of wheat

■ How do these flours differ from each other?

▶ **Strong flour** produces the types and amount of gluten which gives the high volume and open texture properties desired in some products such as good bread, puff pastry and Yorkshire puddings.
▶ **Soft flour** is made from wheat with a lower protein content and is used for products such as cakes and scones, in which a high rise and fine texture are required.
▶ **Plain flour** is sometimes called all-purpose flour and is milled for use in shortcrust pastry, sauces, gravy, etc.
▶ **Self-raising flour** has raising agent evenly mixed into it, which makes it suitable for cakes, puddings etc.
▶ **Patent flours**, often sub-divided into top-patent, long-patent and short-patent, are terms used in the bakery trade. Today these terms are used by millers to identify a particular blend or grade of extra fine white flour, normally of 50–65 per cent extraction.

### Hard-wheat semolina

During milling processes known as **purification and reduction** take place. In these processes granular particles (called **semolina**) are produced. Hard-wheat semolina is used to make pasta. The description 'semolina di grano duro' appears on packets of good Italian dried pasta. This means that the pasta is produced from durum wheat which is a very hard-grain high-protein variety of wheat. Semolina is a word derived from *semila*, the Latin for fine flour in the sense of good quality.

To make pasta successfully it must be dried without splintering and when cooked must remain firm and not become mushy. The high-protein, hard-grain durum wheat is ideal and the flour in semolina form absorbs less water than a more finely ground (smaller particle size) product and consequently forms a dough which dries quickly and does not splinter.

# Rice

Other cereals are also used as raw materials from which products are developed. Rice is one example, although usually it is eaten whole. As a result the milling process is simpler. When only the outer hull of the grain is removed brown rice results. When the germ and the bran are removed and the remaining grain is polished white rice results. Sometimes raw rice is soaked in warm water (sometimes under pressure) for a few hours and then dried and cooled. Rice treated in this way is described as parboiled and is less likely to be damaged during processing. Parboiled rice also has a higher vitamin content than rice which has not been parboiled.

# Fruit and vegetables

The nature of fruit and vegetables means that they continue to ripen after picking and can quickly deteriorate in quality as a result. The ripening takes place as the fruit and vegetables absorb oxygen, give off carbon dioxide and generate heat when light is present. If ripening did not take place the fruit and vegetables would be inedible. Storage conditions and processing techniques therefore need to be managed, to make sure the fruit and vegetables are of the quality the consumer demands.

### Processing vegetables

Before being cooked, good quality vegetables require a minimum of processing, for example, washing and trimming. However, vegetables are grown all over the world now and transported over long distances. Sometimes slight refrigeration is used to keep them in good condition because it slows the ripening rate. Other methods include deep (quick) freezing. Some crops are grown especially for deep (quick) freezing e.g. peas and beans.

Other vegetables are preserved by canning or pickling or made into soups, sauces etc. In these cases the primary processing techniques involve cleaning, trimming, peeling and cutting to the required shape and size (the particle size).

### Processing fruit

Fruit is also transported all over the world. For example, bananas come from Central America, oranges from South America and so on. Fruit easily goes mouldy because it has a fairly high sugar content, so great care is required to make sure good quality fruit is available all the year round. One way is to control the atmosphere in which fruit is transported and stored. In this instance oxygen in the atmosphere is reduced and carbon dioxide is increased to slow ripening. The fruit is sealed in plastic containers and the gases are injected into the containers in the required amounts.

Another way is to use cool conditions in which the fruit is transported, e.g. refrigerated containers or trucks which are kept above freezing. Some fruit need a higher temperature than this. For example, bananas are kept cool but slightly above refrigeration temperatures.

## Tasks

'Take Five' is a slogan recently introduced to encourage people to include more fruit and vegetables in their daily diet in order to gain a healthier balance of foods.

1 a Show how simple it is to fit five servings of fruit and vegetables (five in total, not five of each) into a normal day's eating by suggesting what could be included for one person for breakfast, mid-morning break, lunch and evening meal.

b Name the fruit and vegetables each time.

c State the serving size in each case (Do not include potatoes as these are classed as starchy foods in the 'balanced plate', see page 52.)

One serving (or portion) can be based on one of the following:
▸ 2 tablespoons of vegetables
▸ 2 tablespoons stewed fruit (or canned)
▸ 100 ml fruit juice
▸ one piece fresh fruit
▸ small salad.

2 Design and make a dish based on vegetables which would serve two people for their evening meal on their return from work. The dish should be capable of being re-heated without loss of flavour and texture (for example crispness).

## Meat, poultry and fish

Meat, poultry and fish must be processed to ensure that:

▶ products are of the highest quality
▶ products are free from parasitic infestation and fungal and bacterial infections.

Meat must be 'aged' to allow the muscle to relax, otherwise it will be tough and not have the tender quality demanded by consumers. Meat products such as sausages are processed further to produce the form and quality characteristics of the product.

Fish deteriorates more quickly than meat. This is because there is a chemical substance in fish flesh which stops the flesh becoming acid. This substance allows microbes (bacteria) to grow and this in turn spoils the fish. The chemical substance is called **trimethylamine oxide (TMO)**. Microbes in the fish flesh change TMO to another substance called **trimethylamine (TMA)**. This has a rotten-fish smell. The microbes (bacteria) in fish grow even at normal refrigeration temperature (i.e. between 0° and 5°C). Fish therefore, must be preserved, at lower temperatures. It is recommended that fish is stored at –5°C, within an hour of catching, and then at –10°C within two hours. This is why there are ships with refrigeration plants in deep-sea fishing fleets. The fish are gutted and cleaned first and then coated with ice. This is called **glazing**. They are then frozen to –10°C within two hours and then stored at temperatures below –18°C.

Fatty or oily fish such as mackerel and herring become rancid quickly as a result of the fat in their flesh.

Other methods of processing fish include smoking, salting and canning.

Fish fingers are produced from slabs of frozen fish. The slab could be made from a particular fish, such as cod, or from a mixture of minced fish. Fish fingers made from one fish type only tend to have a better eating quality.

## Vegetable oils and fats

Vegetable oils and fats are extracted from cereals, nuts and plants such as corn and olives. The process is rather complicated but, put simply, the oil is extracted and then refined and clarified. The process is very carefully controlled to make sure the highest quality product results. The oil from olives is produced by pressing the stoned and peeled fruit at room temperature. A special press must be used because considerable pressure has to be exerted.

## Milk

Milk is a naturally-occurring emulsion of fat (oil) in water. Primary processes used here are concerned with making the milk safe to drink, and must involve heat. Approximately 99 per cent of milk sold in the UK today is heat treated. The three main methods are:

▶ pasteurization
▶ ultra-heat treated (UHT)
▶ sterilization.

Some heat-treated milks are homogenized. This process breaks up the fat globules to a uniform size. These remain evenly distributed throughout the milk (i.e. there is no creamy topping).

### Pasteurized milk

This process is a mild form of heat treatment which makes the milk safe to drink. This is because the temperature reached ensures that any bacteria present are killed. Neither the nutritional value nor the flavour of the milk is affected to any great extent. About ten per cent of each of the thiamin and Vitamin B12 is destroyed and 25 per cent of the vitamin C is destroyed. Vitamin C may also be destroyed during storage, but milk is not used as a rich source of vitamin C in the diet so these losses are not really significant. In the HTST (high temperature, short time) process the milk is heated to a temperature of not less than 71.7°C for at least 15 seconds. Immediately the heating is finished, the milk is cooled to not more than 10°C in a heat exchanger (sometimes called a pasteurizer) and then further cooled to about 3°C.

Other types of processed milk include:

▶ dried milk and milk powders
▶ evaporated and condensed milks
▶ filled milk (skimmed milk to which vegetable fat has been added)
▶ fermented milk e.g. buttermilk, yoghurt.

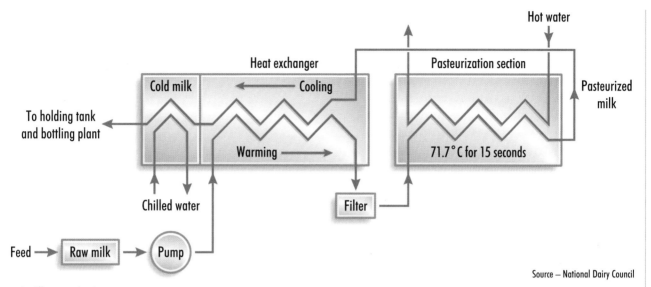

■ A milk pasteurization system

Source – National Dairy Council

# Sugar

Sugar is made from sugar-cane or sugar-beet. Sugar-beet provides about one third of the sugar used in the UK. During the processing of white sugar (sucrose) a variety of forms of sugar result:
▶ brown sugar – a crystallized raw sugar with colours and flavours added after it has been separated from a thick liquid called molasses, which is produced during processing
▶ treacle and golden syrup – produced when the molasses and residue from early refining are further refined.

# Coffee, tea and cocoa

Coffee beans are the seeds of the coffee tree. They are found in the fruit of the tree, called the coffee cherry. After early processing to remove the beans from the cherry, the beans (which are green at this stage) are roasted. Their colour changes to various degrees of brown, and this is the stage when the flavour develops. The beans are cooled quickly and packed, often in a vacuum to preserve flavour and quality. The different flavours of coffee are produced by different beans that are either used alone or blended with other varieties, and by the degree of roasting.

Tea leaves are the young shoots of the tea bush. Harvesting tea leaves is labour-intensive because it is almost always done by hand. The leaves are dried and crushed and then kept at a temperature of between 20 °C and 25 °C for about three hours. They are then dried on heated steel trays and their colour changes from green to black. The leaves are packed in tea chests for transporting and then put into packets by the retailer. There are many different types of tea, each with a characteristic taste, strength and aroma when infused with boiling water.

Cocoa beans (sometimes called nibs) are picked, and then treated with water contaminated with yeast, which helps to develop the flavour and remove a pulp which coats the beans. They are then roasted and ground. This produces cocoa mass which is used in the production of chocolate and cocoa powder.

## Task

3 Coffee, tea and cocoa are used to flavour products in addition to their uses as drinks.
   a Carry out research into recipes where one of these is used as an ingredient.
   b Choose one of the recipes you have found. Make up the recipe.
   c Write an advertising slogan which aims to inform consumers about the flavouring potential of the product you have used.

## Changing raw materials into products - secondary processing

### Baked products

Baked products provide rich opportunities for food manufacturers because they are popular with consumers. The table below shows the consumption, in grams per person per week, of cakes and biscuits and bread in 1994.

| Product | Grams per person per week | | |
|---|---|---|---|
| | Eaten outside the home | Household | Total |
| Cakes and biscuits | 42 | 261 | 303 |
| Bread | 76 | 758 | 834 |

Source – Adapted from MAFF, *National Food Survey*, 1994

The cakes and biscuits eaten included buns, scones, tea-cakes, cakes, pastries and biscuits including chocolate biscuits. The bread eaten included sandwiches and filled rolls. Baked products are made domestically using a great variety of recipes. In commercial food manufacturing the aim is to produce similar products of consistent quality which will be popular with the consumer.

## Cakes and biscuits

The basic ingredients used are flour, fat, sugar and eggs. Many mixtures also have a raising agent and flavourings added. The flavourings and the proportions of one ingredient to another produce the wide variety in types of biscuits and cakes available. The basic ingredients each help to create the properties required in making successful products.

### The properties of ingredients

▶ **Flour** gives a baked product its structure.
▶ **Fats** create properties which add flavour and give mouth-feel (see page 103) to products. Cooking fats are manufactured to make them suitable for particular purposes, for example a gas is whipped into some fats during manufacture which makes them easier to cream.

Shortening fats contain emulsifying agents which limit gluten development in cake and biscuit mixtures, thus producing a shorter, more tender crumb. High-ratio fats are also produced. These allow for the emulsification of more water than other fats. When used in cake mixtures they allow a sweeter and longer-lasting product to be made because extra water and sugar can be added successfully to the mixture. Cooking oils are used because they have little or no flavour and generally have a high smoke point (i.e. they can be heated to a high temperature before breaking down and producing acrid fumes and an unpleasant odour).

▶ **Sugar** gives sweetness and bulk to a mixture. Colour also develops as a result of sugar. Because sugar has good water-holding capacity (it is a good **humectant**), it delays the drying and staling of a baked product. However, in a microwave oven, sugar is heated rapidly so if cooking is done by this method great care must be taken not to spoil the product.
▶ **Egg yolks** contain fat which enriches a mixture. Lecithin, the emulsifier found in egg yolk, stabilizes the cake or biscuit mixture (most mixtures are emulsions of fat in liquid).

### Raising agents

Air can be beaten into mixtures. For example, when fat and sugar are creamed together, air is added. In mixtures containing eggs a foam is produced when the mixture is beaten. This foam contains air. Air expands when heated and raises the product.

Baking powder produces carbon dioxide gas in a mixture when mixed with moisture and heated. This gas expands on heating and raises the product.

The characteristics of the final product depend on the mix and proportion of ingredients and the processing method. For example, the keeping quality or shelf-life of a cake is increased when fat is added. It is decreased when no fat is used. A fatless sponge cake is a good example of this. When it is first made, it is light and tender but soon after it becomes dry and unappetizing.

## ═ Task ═

4 a Prepare:
  (i) a Victoria sandwich cake by the creaming or all-in-one method
  (ii) a whisked fat-less sponge cake.
  b Compare the two using the following headings.
  (i) Texture and crumb on cooling
  (ii) Texture and crumb one day after making
  c What do you notice? Record your observations.
  d Look at a similar pair of commercially produced cakes.
  (i) Compare them for texture and crumb with the ones you have made. What are the differences?
  (ii) Use the ingredients lists to help you explain any differences.

## Pastries

The basic ingredients for pastries are flour, fat and water. Different pastries use the basic ingredients in different ways and in different proportions. The strength of flour used differs according to the type of pastry being produced. For example, for puff and other flaky pastries, a strong flour with a high gluten content is required to provide the elasticity needed when rolling and folding the pastry. For short pastry a flour with less gluten is required because if the dough for this pastry is too elastic the product will be tough.

The fat used makes the product tender. In the case of a short pastry, it gives a 'melt in the mouth' feel. Fats have a shortening effect, they coat the starch and gluten in the flour and break up the structure to produce this effect. Fats are also chosen for use in pastry making according to their capacity to spread. This is known as **plasticity**.

## ═ Task ═

5 a Look up recipes and methods for:
  ▶ short crust pastry
  ▶ flaky pastry (or rough-puff)
  ▶ choux pastry.
  b List the differences between them (e.g. the type and proportions of ingredients, the handling of the ingredients).
  c List the 'points of care' from the methods given for each pastry. These are the points to follow to make sure the product is a success,
  d Choose one of the pastries. Draw a flow diagram to show the stages in making it. Make the pastry. Record the points of care on the flow diagram at the relevant stages of making. These points are where you are 'controlling' what is happening to the ingredients to make a successful product.

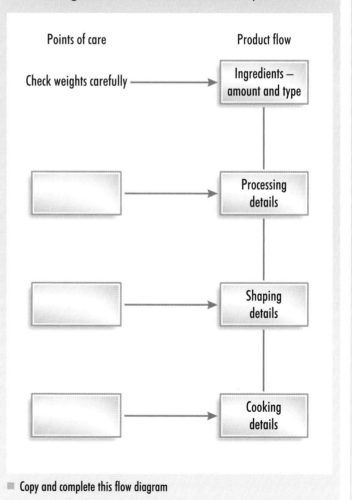

■ Copy and complete this flow diagram

# Breads

Many different breads are made commercially. Some are risen or **leavened**, others such as pitta bread, chapatis, naan bread and pumpernickel (a kind of black bread from Germany) are **unleavened**. All breads are mixtures of flour and water and those that are leavened are **aerated** (small bubbles of air and carbon dioxide are enclosed in the dough). The carbon dioxide is produced by yeast fermentation (see page 65).

*Breadmaking*

In large-scale production of bread there are three methods which can be used for preparing dough prior to baking. They are:

▸ the **bulk fermentation process (BFP)** – This is a long process because it relies on the dough being left to ferment for up to two hours. Increasingly, large-scale bakers do not have time for this.

▸ **activated dough development (ADD)** – Reducing agents are used to change the dough in the same ways as fermentation and mixing do.

▸ The **Chorleywood bread process (CBP)** – This is the most commonly-used method for large-scale production today. It involves the addition of **improvers** (usually ascorbic acid, vitamin C) and a few minutes of intensive mechanical mixing. This produces the elasticity needed in the dough much more quickly than the other two methods.

Other ways in which fermentation is speeded up in industry include:

▸ using stronger yeasts which produce larger amounts of carbon dioxide
▸ using very powerful machines for mixing
▸ adding small amounts of very hard fat which coats the gas bubbles and does not melt at the temperatures which occur in the dough
▸ using emulsifiers to help the ingredients to mix and make sure the fat is dispersed in the starch gel of the dough.

## Task

6 Yeast is easily destroyed by heat. Fermentation cannot take place if the yeast is destroyed. Find out how and why yeast is destroyed. Write a list of things to do which would prevent this happening during breadmaking.

(Your teacher may be able to give you experiment sheet 5c to help you.)

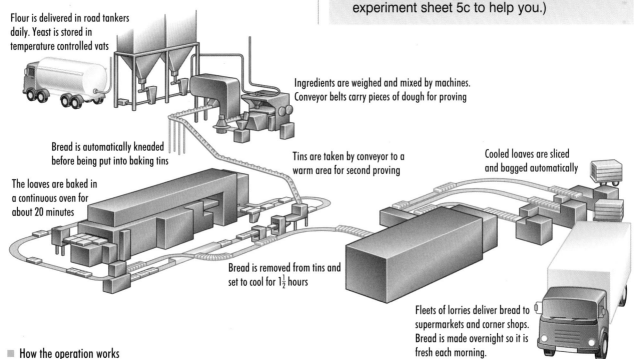

Flour is delivered in road tankers daily. Yeast is stored in temperature controlled vats

Ingredients are weighed and mixed by machines. Conveyor belts carry pieces of dough for proving

Bread is automatically kneaded before being put into baking tins

Tins are taken by conveyor to a warm area for second proving

Cooled loaves are sliced and bagged automatically

The loaves are baked in a continuous oven for about 20 minutes

Bread is removed from tins and set to cool for $1\frac{1}{2}$ hours

Fleets of lorries deliver bread to supermarkets and corner shops. Bread is made overnight so it is fresh each morning.

■ How the operation works

Commercial breadmaking is a very technical process where both temperature and time have to be carefully controlled in order to produce good quality bread. Throughout the history of breadmaking developments have helped to improve the quality of bread. Bread improvers which are based on **oxidizing agents** are now widely used in the baking industry. By and large these are chemical in nature and have two functions:

▶ to increase the ability of gluten in the dough to stretch
▶ to whiten flour (sometimes called **bleaching**).

*Bread descriptions*

Here are some of the descriptions used for bread.
▶ Wholemeal bread must be made only from wholemeal flour (and contain not less than 2.2 per cent crude fibre).
▶ Brown bread must contain not less than 0.6 per cent crude fibre. Some brown breads have caramel added to give more colour and flavour.

## — *Task* —

7 a Carry out a survey to find out:
    (i) the most popular type of loaf bought in a small bakery
    (ii) the most popular type of loaf bought in a local supermarket.
  b Collate the results of your survey to find out if there is a difference. If there is a difference, how big is it?
  c Do your figures reflect the percentages shown in the pie chart below?

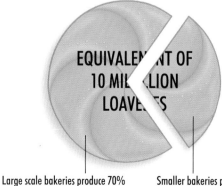

EQUIVALENT OF 10 MILLION LOAVES

Large scale bakeries produce 70%    Smaller bakeries produce 30%

■ Daily production of bread and morning goods in the UK

## Rice products

Examples of secondary products from rice include easy-cook and quick-cook rice. During processing the grain is cracked so that when the rice is cooked water is absorbed more easily and quickly.

## — *Task* —

8 a Look at the cooking instructions given on a packet of ordinary rice and a packet of easy-cook rice. Notice the time recommendations.
  b Comment upon the difference.
  c Cook 50 g of each rice. Compare the eating quality of each sample.

## Other products

Breakfast cereals such as puffed rice from rice, and cornflakes from corn are examples of products made from secondary processing techniques. Other examples include:
▶ margarine and many low-fat spreads
▶ butter and cheese from milk
▶ many snack foods, e.g. potato crisps.

## Extruded products

Extruders are machines which force a paste through plates with holes in them. Most pastes are made from wheat starch and potato starch. These pastes are 'extruded' and then cooked, flavoured and coloured to produce a variety of snack foods. Sometimes the final product is puffed up by having air added to it. Some breakfast cereals are made in this way. The cooking method for the extruded material is often flash-frying and the flavour is often made stronger by the addition of salt.

## — *Task* —

9 a Find a snack food which has been produced by extrusion.
  b Record what you think bring about its appearance, taste and colour.
  c Look at the ingredients label. Record what the product is made of.

## Hazard Analysis Critical Control Point (HACCP)

Control systems are used to make sure a product is safe, legal and consistent.

All control systems involve:

▸ identifying hazards which could occur at all stages of the development (i.e. the risks)

▸ identifying the controls which would eliminate or minimize the risks.

This is called Hazard Analysis Critical Control Point (HACCP). It is internationally recognized as the most effective way to maximize product safety.

## Why did the HACCP system begin?

There is a story – which may or may not be true – that says that HACCP started when American space exploration began. The food which was to be eaten in space had to be totally 'hazard-free', people had to be sure that there was nothing in the food which would cause sickness. All the things which could go wrong were identified and an enormous list of possible hazards was prepared. Every possible check for pests, bacteria and any other extraneous material and of the processing methods was carried out to eliminate all hazards. The approach was:

▸ Hazard analysis (HA)

▸ Elimination and prevention of hazards at particular points of processing and storage (CCP)

Thus HACCP was born!

## The seven steps to safe products

1 **Hazard analysis** Details of production are entered on a flow diagram with the risks (hazards) and points of care (control mechanisms) included.
2 The points where the hazards must be controlled are identified as **critical control points** or CCPs for short.
3 Each CCP must have limits within which safety is ensured (called **tolerance levels**).
4 The CCPs are tested and monitored.
5 A system to 'put things right' if faults occur must be included (called **corrective action**).
6 Records must be kept of all processes, results and corrective actions.
7 Periodic and on-going tests must be carried out to make sure the HACCP is effective. This is called an **audit**.

In food product development the three areas that must be considered in terms of food safety are:

▸ the raw materials used

▸ the processing methods used

▸ the way in which a product is designed to be used.

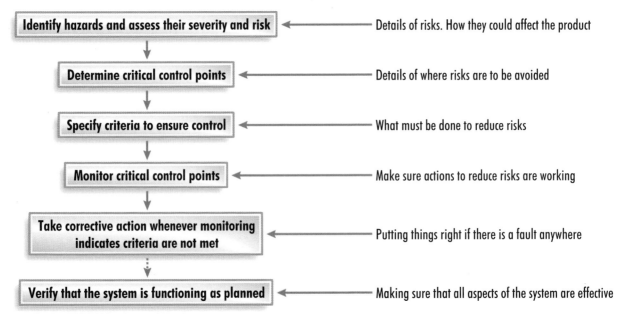

| | |
|---|---|
| **Identify hazards and assess their severity and risk** | Details of risks. How they could affect the product |
| **Determine critical control points** | Details of where risks are to be avoided |
| **Specify criteria to ensure control** | What must be done to reduce risks |
| **Monitor critical control points** | Make sure actions to reduce risks are working |
| **Take corrective action whenever monitoring indicates criteria are not met** | Putting things right if there is a fault anywhere |
| **Verify that the system is functioning as planned** | Making sure that all aspects of the system are effective |

■ The HACCP system represented as a flow diagram

Source – Adapted from F. L. Bryan, *Hazard Analysis Critical Control Point Evaluations*

In processing, the hazards depend upon:
▶ the source of ingredients
▶ the recipe formulation
▶ the equipment used
▶ how long processing takes
▶ storage of the product
▶ the experience and attitudes of the personnel involved in production (the handling of food).

In addition the degree of risk varies depending on:
▶ the food source
▶ methods used to prepare the foods
▶ the conditions in which foods are kept hot or cold
▶ the time between cooking and eating.

**Process control** is used to monitor measurement in product development. The system used is **Computer Integrated Manufacture** where automatic adjustments can be made at critical manufacturing points. If these adjustments are not made products will be unsaleable. Monitoring provides feedback to the system and allows adjustments to be made if necessary. The measurements made include:
▶ the weight of ingredients
▶ the rate at which a mixture or ingredients flow through a system
▶ the temperature

▶ the pressure
▶ the pH
▶ the moisture content
▶ speed of conveyer belt.

An example of computerized process control occurs in the use of chocolate for coating a product. The temperature of the chocolate must be just right, so that the chocolate flows and is the correct consistency to coat the product evenly. If the temperature of the chocolate is too low it will not flow, if the temperature is too high the chocolate spoils and often becomes hardened which again means it will not flow.

Details of the temperature range are fed into the computer which is attached to a sensor in the system. The sensor monitors the temperature of the chocolate and is programmed to switch the heat source on or off according to whether the chocolate has reached the required temperature or has cooled to below the required temperature.

## How does HACCP work in practice?

1 The example in the illustration below is of computerization in large bakeries.

Large bakeries are run by computer systems which enable all the different types of bread to be handled through the system. By the press of buttons the amount/type of flour, temperature of ovens and cooling times can be regulated.

An engineer, responsible for making sure everything runs properly, checks the computer print out sheets at intervals. She/he is able to locate any fault in the system, and also check that the right ingredients are being used for the different breads.

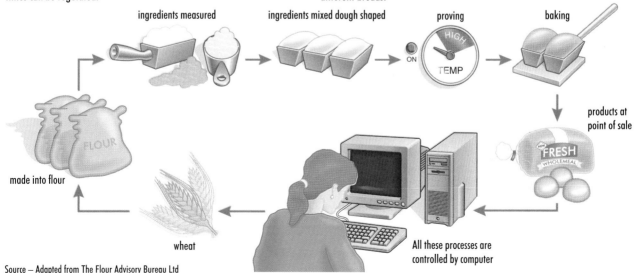

ingredients measured    ingredients mixed dough shaped    proving    baking

products at point of sale

made into flour

wheat

All these processes are controlled by computer

**2** This example is of a cook-chill ready meal system. Notice in the diagram opposite where some processes are low risk and where other processes are high risk.

---

**Ready meals are complicated to produce and throughout the process safety is very important. The following points must be carefully controlled.**

**1** Suitable raw materials must be used.

**2** Raw materials must be treated appropriately so that food poisoning organisms are destroyed.

**3** Cooked ingredients must be cooled quickly.

**4** Meals must be put together in a 'high risk' environment to minimize contamination.

**5** Short shelf-life in chilled distribution.

---

### Critical Control Points for cook-chill ready meals

| | |
|---|---|
| **1** Raw materials | Risk assessment must be carried out to ensure the safety of raw materials. These must be stored correctly and used within shelf-life. |
| **2** Preparation | Material must be stored correctly and used within a specified time to minimize spoilage. |
| **3** Cooking | Food must be cooked to a minimum temperature of 70°C for 2 minutes, or equivalent. |
| **4** Cooling | Product should be cooled to less than 5°C as quickly as possible (typically less than 4 hours). |
| **5** Assembly | This should be carried out in a 'high risk' area to minimize contamination. |
| **6** Packaging | Packaging must provide clear storage and cooking instructions, short shelf-life (typically 8 days). |
| **7** Distribution | Products must be kept at a temperature of less than 5°C during distribution. |

---

### Requirements of a high risk area

**1** It must be an enclosed area.

**2** Must have positive pressure filtered air.

**3** Restricted entry, with 'high risk' clothes changing procedure.

**4** It must be temperature controlled, usually less than 12°C.

**5** Careful cleaning procedures and monitoring of hygiene.

Source – Courtesy of J. Sainsbury plc

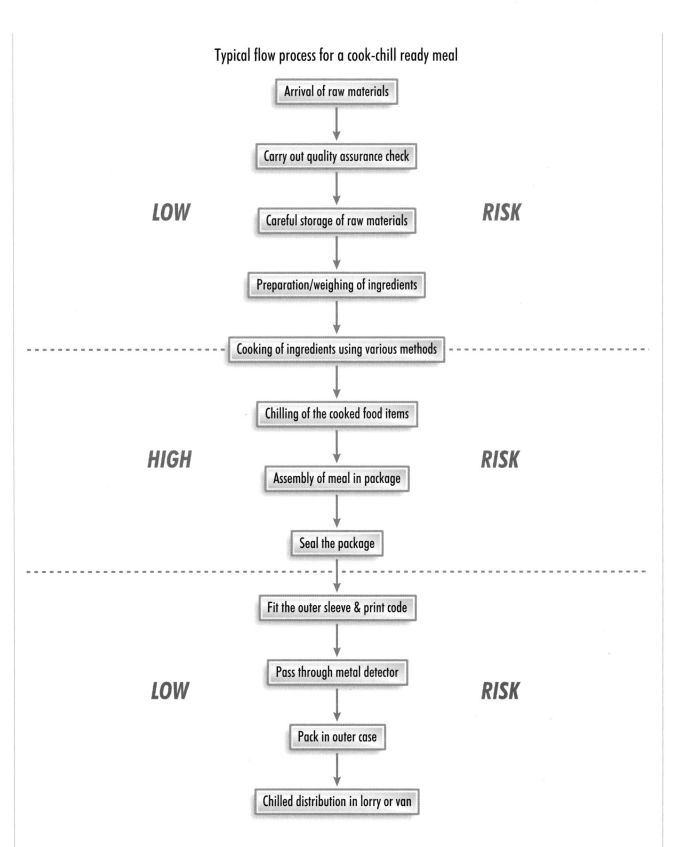

Typical flow process for a cook-chill ready meal

Arrival of raw materials

Carry out quality assurance check

*LOW*      Careful storage of raw materials      *RISK*

Preparation/weighing of ingredients

Cooking of ingredients using various methods

Chilling of the cooked food items

*HIGH*      Assembly of meal in package      *RISK*

Seal the package

Fit the outer sleeve & print code

Pass through metal detector

*LOW*      Pack in outer case      *RISK*

Chilled distribution in lorry or van

*C*ritical control points are specified in the processing system used for a particular product. The details of control are input to a computerized system and then the system is checked at regular intervals to make sure it is working properly.

An example of this is a system which is set up to deliver a particular weight of an ingredient, for example 100 g. Checking to see if the correct weight is being delivered is called **verification**. A **tolerance** is built into the system which allows for slight variations either side of 100 g to be acceptable. For our example, the figure below shows an acceptable tolerance:

```
   98 g         100 g         102 g
    ┕━━━━━ tolerance limits ━━━━━┙
```

Any weight above below 98 g or above 102 g is beyond the tolerance in this system and would be rejected by the system. Then action would be needed. The figure below shows this:

```
   97 g      98 g     100 g    102 g      103 g
beyond limits  ┕━━ tolerance limits ━━┙  beyond limits
action required                          action required
```

Systems such as this are automated once the control point details are input to the computer.

## Types of systems

Most systems are **closed loop** systems. The samples taken to check the effectiveness of the system provide **feedback** information. When the feedback gives information that the system is working well, no action is needed. When the feedback shows that the system is not working well a decision has to made about how seriously out of control the system is, and what adjustments or calculations are needed to put the system back in control.

The table below shows some of the critical control points in food service systems.

This is what the table headings mean and why there may be critical control points.

▸ **Receipt** When the foods are received ready for processing, assembling or serving they should be checked for quality, temperature, appearance, any damage to packaging and, where relevant, pH. This checking allows any risks to be identified and requirements for safe storage and processing to be decided.

▸ **Formulation** This refers to the recipe, that is the type and proportions of ingredients to be used in order that any risks associated with this can be identified.

▸ **Handling of raw ingredients** This means that foods should be checked to establish, for example, that if frozen food has to be thawed then it is thawed safely and effectively; if food is to be served without re-heating or cooking then its temperature is appropriate etc. This means that potential contamination points can be identified.

▸ **Cooking** The highest temperature reached in the centre of foods should be measured and where relevant the time the food is kept at a particular temperature should be checked to ensure that bacteria cannot survive the cooking process.

▸ **Hot-holding** The time during which hot foods are kept hot should be controlled and the temperature should be checked.

### Common critical control points in food service systems

| System | Receipt | Formulation | Handling of raw ingredients | Cooking | Hot-holding | Cooling | Handling of cooked products | Reheating |
|---|---|---|---|---|---|---|---|---|
| Cook/serve | | | | X | | | X* | |
| Prepare/serve cold | X | X* | X | | | X | | |
| Cook/hold hot | | | | X | X | | X | |
| Cook/chill | | | | X | | X | X | X |
| Cook/frezze | | | | X | | X | X | X |
| Assemble/serve | X | | | | | | X | X |

**\* Sometimes a critical control point**

Source – Adapted from E. L. Bryan, *Hazard Analysis Critical Control Point Evaluations*

▶ **Cooling** The depth of the food to be cooled should be checked as should the various temperatures during cooling. For example if food is cooled very slowly there is risk of contamination from the multiplication of bacteria.

▶ **Handling of cooled products** There is risk of contamination both from the environment (i.e. room temperature) and from the people who are handling the food.

▶ **Reheating** The highest temperature reached in the centre of foods must be measured, as must the times and temperatures operating during reheating.

## Micro-organisms and HACCP

In product development it is important to apply knowledge of the type of micro-organisms which contaminate the foods being used. For example knowledge of the conditions under which the micro-organisms multiply and thrive must be applied in order that appropriate critical points of control can be built into the processing system. This will ensure that:

▶ waste is minimized to the lowest level possible

▶ products are safe to eat

▶ products are of the required quality.

Micro-organisms can alter the texture, aroma and flavour of food if conditions suit them. Worse still, there are some micro-organisms which can make food unsafe to eat. These organisms cause food poisoning. The main micro-organisms are:

▶ **bacteria**   ▶ **yeasts**   ▶ **moulds**.

All three of these categories cause food spoilage and bacteria cause food poisoning. The critical control points which are built into a food production system must limit food spoilage and prevent the growth of bacteria. Growth refers to the fact that the bacteria increase in number under the right conditions – they multiply.

## Controlling food spoilage

Yeasts and moulds can be useful in the production of some foods. For example, some blue cheeses have mould injected into them to produce their characteristic colour and flavour. Stilton is a good example of this. Yeast is used in breadmaking to good effect.

Both yeasts and moulds need moisture to flourish. Moulds need less moisture than yeasts. Moulds have a fuzzy, hair-like appearance and can make foods unfit to eat.

Yeasts are always present in the air. They mainly grow on sugary foods. Bubbles of gas, carbon dioxide and a small amount of alcohol are present when yeasts are growing. This is called fermentation.

The photos below show a sequence of food spoilage. Spoilage can be minimized or prevented during product development, processing and distribution by controlling:

▶ the moisture in the environment e.g. storing 'at-risk' foods, in dry conditions. At-risk foods include bread, fruits, sugary products e.g. jam.

▶ the temperature at which foods are stored, processed and distributed, e.g. moulds and yeasts grow best at temperatures of 20–40°C and are destroyed at the temperature at which water boils (100°C) and above.

▶ the standards of cleanliness of the environment in which product development and processing takes place and of the personnel involved.

■ The gradual deterioration of a bowl of fruit

# Controlling food poisoning

Various types of bacteria cause food poisoning.
▶ Species of salmonella (e.g. S. *typhi*) multiply in food and infect the people eating it. High-risk foods include eggs, chicken, meat, milk and cream etc.
▶ *Staphylococcus aureus, Clostridium botulinum, Clostridium perfringens* multiply in food and produce toxins which cause food poisoning. The toxin produced by *Clostridium botulinum* produces very serious food poisoning which can kill. High-risk foods include vegetables (including pulses), chicken and meat dishes, fish dishes.
▶ Other bacteria which cause food poisoning include B*acillus cereus* which also produces a toxin in the food. Rice and some shell fish are high-risk foods here.
▶ *Campylobacter* can also cause food poisoning. The high-risk foods here are those from animal sources, including milk.
▶ Listeria (*Listeria monocyotogenes*) is a food poisoning organism which puts cook-chill products at risk because it can multiply rapidly at temperatures above 4°C. Other foods at risk include salads, pâtés and goats cheeses.
▶ The critical aspect to consider in the control of food poisoning is temperature. In addition to temperature control, high standards of cleanliness and hygiene by the personnel and in the processing environment must be maintained.

This information needs to be applied in product development when:
▶ storing raw materials and products
▶ preparing and cooking food
▶ cooling products
▶ serving and packing products
▶ transporting products
▶ displaying products.

The table opposite shows hazards which you should bear in mind during product development work and the control and monitoring actions you should take to avoid the risks associated with those hazards.

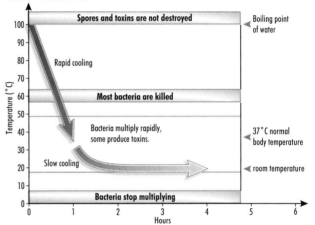

Source – © 1985 A. G. Cameron. Reproduced with permission
Hodder & Stoughton Educational Ltd

■ The rate at which food cools. Note that it remains in the danger zone (where bacteria multiply rapidly) for a long time

| The effects of temperature (°C) on food | |
|---|---|
| 240 230 | Grilling |
| 220 | Baking |
| 180 | Shallow frying |
| 120 | Bacterial spores killed (3 minutes) |
| 100 | Water boils |
| 95 | Starch gelatinizes |
| 90 70 | Roasting |
| 70 | Protein denatures |
| | Living bacteria and yeat killed (not spores) |
| 60 | Serving temperature |
| 50 | Below this temperature bacteria thrive |
| 5 | Maximum refrigerator temperature |
| | Vegetable storage |
| 0 | Water freezes |
| −10 | Seven days freezer storage |
| −20 | One month's freezer storage |
| −30 | Three months' or more freezer storage |

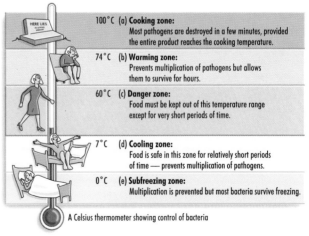

A Celsius thermometer showing control of bacteria

■ The temperature zones. Temperature control is an effective way to kill bacteria or limit their growth

Critical control points, hazards and monitoring actions for some common food operations

| Operation/ critical control point | Risks & hazards | How to avoid hazards | Checking |
|---|---|---|---|
| Purchase/receipt | Micro-organisms on raw foods; foods obtained from unsafe sources | Obtain foods from safe source | Set purchase specifications and check they are met |
| Frozen storage | Microbial growth in thawed goods | Maintain frozen until use | Observe whether foods are frozen; measure temperature of freezer |
| Refrigerated storage | Microbial growth if temperatures too high or duration of storage too long; cross-contamination | Maintain cold temperature; rotate stock | Observe condition of food; measure food and storage temperature, observe storage practices; measure duration of storage; look for potential routes of contamination |
| Dry storage | Break in package; high moisture; poisons stored near foods | Maintain low temperature and humidity; store poisons elsewhere; protect foods from contamination | Observe storage practices |
| Thawing | Bacterial growth; contamination of area by thaw water; incomplete thawing | Thaw at temperatures and within times that do not permit multiplication of common pathogenic bacteria | Observe thawing practice; feel whether product completely thawed |
| Reconstitution (rehydration) | Contamination during rehydration; bacterial growth | Use safe water and clean utensils and containers; use food promptly or refrigerate in small volumes | Observe practices |
| Preparation | Cross-contamination from raw products; contamination from hands, equipment, or utensils | Avoid handling raw foods and then cooked foods; avoid touching foods that are not to heated subsequently | Observe practices |
| Cooking | Bacteria survive inadequate time-temperature exposure; spores survive | Adequate time-temperature exposure | Measure temperature at centre of food |
| Handling of foods that are not subsequently heated | Cross-contamination from raw products; contamination from hands, equipment or utensils | Avoid handling raw foods and then cooked foods; avoid touching foods that are not to be heated subsequently; exclude ill persons from working with food; ensure personal hygiene of food service workers | Observe practices; observe personnel for signs of illness; receive reports of illness or siginificant symptoms |
| Holding at room or warm outside temperatures | Bacterial growth | Limit time of such hoolding; hold hot or cool | Observe practices; measure time of holding |
| Hot-holding | Bacterial growth | Hold foods at temperatures at which bacteria do not multiply | Measure temperature of foods at intervals |
| Cooling | Bacteria multiply | Cool foods rapidly in shallow containers or use other method of rapid cooling; store as close to freezing as feasible | Measure depth of food; measure temperature of food after cooling; observe storage practices |
| Reheating | Micro-organisms may survive; heat-stable toxins will survive | Adequate time-temperature exposure | Measure temperature at completion of reheating |
| Cleaning of equipment and utensils | Failure to remove micro-organisms from surfaces | Wash, rinse, disinfect | Observe practices; measure concentration of disinfectant solution and contact time |

Source – F. L. Bryan, *Hazard Analysis Critical Control Point Evaluations*

# A reminder about HACCP

**Hazard** means that there is a possibility of:
▶ contamination in the food
▶ the growth and survival of micro-organisms in the food
▶ the production of toxins (poisons) in the food as a result of microbial growth.

**Severity** refers to:
▶ the size (magnitude) of the hazard
▶ the possible results (consequences) of the hazard.

**Risk** refers to the consideration of whether a hazard will occur.

# More details about critical control points

A CCP can be part of a practice, a particular procedure in a process, a particular process or a place where a particular process takes place. The information given at each CCP is very specific and must stop the hazard occurring at that point. An example of this is the pasteurization process, where control of a particular part of the process prevents the hazard completely, for example the temperature to be achieved and the time it should be held at.

An important point to remember is that all CCPs must be controlled. This means that for every CCP there should be specific and detailed information about what is being controlled and how. These details are put together into a specification and become the **criteria** (these criteria are used to indicate whether an operation is under control at a particular control point). The criteria are the limits (tolerances) of particular characteristics of a process, or a formulation, or an activity and so on. They cover the following aspects:
▶ physical – e.g. time, temperature
▶ chemical – e.g. concentrations of solutions such as salt solution, acidic solutions, pH
▶ biological – e.g. bacteria, pests, organisms
▶ sensory – e.g. appearance, colour, consistency.

In a production process these criteria are written out very clearly. In some factories the criteria and CCPs which apply at a particular point in production are printed and placed in a prominent position at that particular point.

## CRITICAL CONTROL POINT
### HANDWEIGH & FOIL BAGGING
– **CALIBRATION**
– **WEIGH EACH BAG**
– **CHECK AGAINST PACKING STANDARD**

### LABELLING & PALLETISING
– **CHECK CORRECT DATE CODE, TEA AND WEIGHT**
– **CHECK AGAINST PACKING STANDARD**

## CRITICAL CONTROL POINT
### METAL DETECTION
– **2mm FERROUS**
– **CHECK AT START UP AND EVERY 60 MINUTES**
– **ENSURE PACKS ARE REJECTED INTO LOCKABLE BIN**
– **RETAIN ANY REJECTED PACKS**

## CRITICAL CONTROL POINT
### SHRINKING, LABELLING AND PALLETISING
**CHECK:**
– **SHRINKFILM**
– **BEST BEFORE/DATE CODE OF OUTER LABEL**
– **PALLET CONFIGURATION**
– **AGAINST PACKING STANDARD**

■ Examples of some of the CCP notices used by the speciality tea and coffee manufacturers Taylors of Harrogate. These are positioned at the relevant points around their factory

These criteria are chosen according to their:
- usefulness
- cost
- manageability (called feasibility in industry).

But above all they must provide a high level of assurance that effective control of hazards is taking place.

# More facts about monitoring and verification

## Monitoring

This is a programme of checks of a system which take place at regular intervals. It is the way in which any out-of-control situation can be spotted. Monitoring must also include the ability to put right (**rectify**) an out-of-control situation before a product is distributed or sold. There are five main ways in which monitoring is carried out. They are:
- observation
- sensory evaluation
- measurement of physical properties
- chemical testing
- examination for micro-organisms.

An example of monitoring is when final products are tested before despatch to make sure they meet the specification. For example, monitoring for texture, is a crisp biscuit crisp enough? Or for taste, is a salty product too salty?

## Verification

This is done both by the manufacturer's quality control staff and the Trading Standards and Environmental Health personnel from outside bodies, such as local authorities. The purpose is to check that the HACCP system is working as planned. The checking includes making sure that:
- all hazards have been spotted (detected)
- all CCPs identified
- criteria are appropriate
- monitoring is effective
- records are kept.

## ▬ Task ▬

1 Imagine you are a quality control supervisor for a manufacturer of cold meat products produced for sale on delicatessen counters.
   a Choose one typical product
   b List the details of the critical control points which would be in place when the product is being packed for delivery to ensure that it is safe to eat.
   c Explain why these points are important.

It is important to understand that not everything involved in product development and processing in the food industry can be carried out in school. Recipe formulation, processing methods and testing procedures must be planned and carried out in relation to the resources available. There are several aspects of product development which require more detailed information than appear elsewhere in this book. They include:

▸ how processing affects the nutrient quality, texture, appearance and flavour of food
▸ the influences which affect people's choice of food
▸ how these influences affect the designing of food products.

## How processing affects food

### Proteins are made up of chains of amino-acids

When proteins are heated these chains unfold and break. Then the proteins are **denatured**. This is an important fact to remember when using a protein food such as meat, for example, because the change in the amino acid chains make the meat less tough and as a consequence easier to chew and digest.

Heating causes protein to **coagulate**. For example, when an egg is heated it sets by coagulation. It is this property which makes eggs have a thickening effect in some products (e.g. custards).

### Carbohydrates, i.e. starches and sugars

Starch forms a gel when it is heated with a liquid and this produces a softer texture. For example, potatoes become softer during cooking because the cell walls separate and the starch gelatinizes.

In dry heat, starch changes to dextrin, and this gives foods an attractive toffee colour (making a piece of toast illustrates this very well).

Sugars caramelize when heated to a high temperature and a 'toffee' like material is produced which has an attractive flavour and colour.

When sugars and protein are both present in a food such as meat, Maillard browning results (see page 71). For example, when a lamb chop is grilled it becomes brown and develops a stronger more tasty flavour on the outside.

### Vitamins are destroyed by heat

This is true for all vitamins, to some extent. The most easily destroyed are described as **unstable** or **heat-liable** vitamins.

Vitamin C is the most unstable of the vitamins. Folate is also more unstable than other vitamins. Vitamin C is also water-soluble and is easily destroyed by heat, even at quite low temperatures. Therefore, when cooking food which supplies vitamin C, care should be taken to use small amounts of liquid, cook the food quickly and serve it straight away.

Care must also be taken when preparing foods which supply vitamin C, since it is destroyed by oxygen in the air. For example, chopping and cutting a vegetable into small pieces increases the surface area in contact with the air, so more vitamin C will be destroyed.

The fat-soluble vitamins such as A and D are not easily destroyed, except at very high temperatures.

Many foods, such as potatoes, cannot be eaten in their raw state, therefore some processing is necessary. Processing methods need to be chosen carefully, however, to ensure that the product remains nutritious and is palatable and tasty and therefore appeals to the consumer.

## The influences which affect choices

### Life-style

People's life-style influences the choices they make. There are many effects of life-style, including:

▸ the amount of money available to spend on food
▸ the amount of time available to prepare food
▸ the type of household – single person, larger family size. (It is predicted that the number of one-person households will have risen to 6.6 million in 2001)
▸ the number of people working in a household. (Figures show that over half of all women aged 16–65 were working, full or part-time in 1994)
▸ increase in car ownership
▸ increase in leisure time and holiday entitlement. (For example, in 1994 people living in the UK took 27 million holidays abroad, compared with 4 million in 1971.)

### The type of community

The type of community in which people live is influenced by:

▷ location, e.g. urban (town), rural (country) and region
▷ cultural and ethnic mix.

### Beliefs and traditions

Food is symbolic in many religions and forms part of the rules of some. Food also plays a central role in some traditional celebrations.

### Age

Age has a tremendous effect on food choice and makes an interesting topic for research.

### Personal preference

Individual likes and dislikes about the appearance, flavour and texture of food will influence choices.

### Advertising

Advertising can exert influence on the consumer and can sometimes have such an effect that supplies of a food product can run out.

### Consumer awareness

Consumers are increasingly aware about certain aspects of food consumption and processing. This can be a very powerful influence, especially in the areas of healthy eating initiatives, fashions in food, 'green' issues, etc.

### Dietary, nutritional and special needs

These play a large part in most people's food choices. The increase in the number of people who are overweight and becoming seriously overweight (obese) means that people generally should pay more attention to the energy value of the foods they eat. For example, the overweight and obese are advised to 'rethink' their food choices and be more willing to be influenced by nutritional and dietary recommendations. Special needs include diabetics and those with coeliac disease.

## How do these affect designing?

All these factors give indications about what the consumer will buy and expect from products.

Influences of life-style need to be researched during 'concept generation', so that where relevant the product is:

▷ priced to suit the target market
▷ convenient to use
▷ packaged to suit all household types, e.g. one-portion sizes as well as larger quantities
▷ quick to prepare
▷ widely available (increase in car ownership means that many consumers can shop anywhere)
▷ interesting and different, not necessarily traditional. Consumers are more adventurous and sophisticated due to foreign travel.

■ Most fish must be cooked to make it palatable and safe to eat. The cooking method must suit the characteristics of the fish so that once cooked it is in the best possible condition for eating. In white fish, the muscle fibres are short, the tissue which joins the muscle together is fragile and the fat content is low. These characteristics mean that white fish should be cooked only to the point when the muscle proteins coagulate and any bacteria present are killed. Beyond this point white fish becomes dry, falls apart and also becomes tough.

■ The energy value of foods can be altered by the cooking method used. For example when foods are fried they absorb some of the fat, and this increases their energy value. Consumers who do not have active lives or who tend to be overweight need to choose cooking methods carefully. For example, raw potatoes supply 350 kJ/87 kcal of energy per 100 g, when made into chips they supply 960 kJ/239 kcal. The potatoes become a high-energy food when fried.

## How available is the evidence?

There are many sources of evidence about consumer needs. Some are called **secondary** sources. These include published material that may be found in books, newspapers, magazines etc. They may be in the form of information, recipes, processing methods or figures such as data produced as a result of research by other people. When using information it is important to select what is useful and relevant to the task in hand.

Another type of evidence is **primary** source material. This is evidence you collect yourself specifically to provide information for the task in hand. There are many ways of doing this including making observations, devising questionnaires, carrying out interviews, having group discussions, trialling products and sensory evaluation.

To ensure that information collected is useful, it is essential that you analyse the task in hand carefully. This analysis will highlight those aspects or factors about which you need more information before you can begin product development.

## Why is research useful?

Research involves collecting as much information as possible about consumer choices and the factors which influence consumer purchasing. This information is collected through **market research**.

There are many companies that specialize in market research. They are asked by various organizations and companies to provide evidence about, for example:

▷ sales and popularity of existing foodstuffs and products
▷ trends in eating and buying food
▷ how popular a new product might be
▷ how effective an advertising campaign is or could be

and so on. They collect information in the ways listed above.

Examples of surveys carried out for food include the MAFF (Ministry of Agriculture, Fisheries and Food) National Food Survey. The following chart is an example of how the information is presented.

One large 'marketing intelligence' company, Mintel, recently examined the market for bread

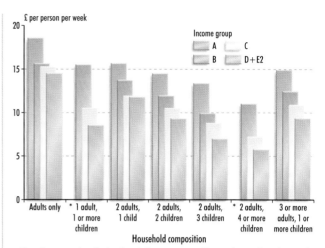

£ per person per week

Income group
A  C
B  D+E2

* Expenditure is not shown for these households in income group A because there are fewer than 10 such households in the sample.

Source – MAFF, *National Food Survey*, 1994

■ Total household food expenditure per head by household composition within income groups, 1994

and 'morning' goods. Morning goods were defined as rolls, baps, buns, muffins, crumpets, scones, teacakes, fruited products and croissants and other foreign semi-sweet breads. The following text is an example of information collected.

---

*Continental and speciality bread*

Continental and ethnic speciality bread is a continuing area of growth. This sub-sector was valued at £30 million in 1989, and Mintel estimates that sales increased to around £65 million during 1994. The wide range of ethnic and continental specialities available fall between the broad classifications of white, brown and wholemeal. French-style breads predominate, and the French baguette is widely available. Other French breads such as pain de campagne are becoming more popular.

Pitta bread, naan and bagels are among other growth areas of the specialities sub-sector. During 1993, some manufacturers reported a 30 per cent increase in demand for bagels although some production will be for the pre-packed sandwich trade.

---

Source – Mintel, *Marketing and Intelligence*, March 1995

The figures that follow were collected during the same survey. They give information about the retail sales of types of morning goods.

### Retail sales of morning goods by type, 1990–4

| | 1990 £m | 1990 % | 1992 £m | 1992 % | 1994 estimated £m | 1994 estimated % | % change 1990–94 |
|---|---|---|---|---|---|---|---|
| *Rolls and baps* | 540 | 65 | 615 | 66 | 694 | 66 | +29 |
| *Buns and teacakes* | 151 | 18 | 159 | 18 | 183 | 17 | +21 |
| *Toasting products* | 75 | 9 | 87 | 9 | 114 | 11 | +52 |
| *Scones* | 42 | 5 | 45 | 5 | 44 | 4 | +4 |
| *Croissants* | 17 | 2 | 19 | 2 | 22 | 2 | +29 |
| *Total* | 825 | 100 | 925 | 100 | 1057 | 100 | +28 |

*Data may not equal totals due to rounding*              Source – Mintel

## What use is this type of information?

When a task involves the need to find evidence of what people spend on food, the Food Survey figures can be helpful. The most recent indicate what households of different family size and income groups spent in 1994. This helps to target the cost of production and the retail price of a product to fit the price likely to attract a particular household.

The Mintel text and figures supply an up-to-date and accurate indication of popular products. These could prompt ideas which could be worth developing into new lines or applications.

Other figures such as those shown below give information about how much is spent by specific household types on particular foods.

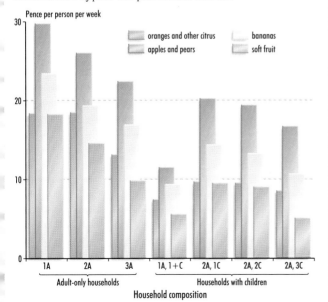

Pence per person per week

oranges and other citrus · apples and pears · bananas · soft fruit

Household composition

Adult-only households: 1A, 2A, 3A
Households with children: 1A, 1+C, 2A, 1C, 2A, 2C, 2A, 3C

Source – MAFF, *National Food Survey*, 1994

■ Expenditure on fresh fruit by household composition, 1994

## What information do these figures give you?

▸ The amount spent per person per week is lower in households of more than one adult.
▸ The amount spent on fresh fruit by households where there are children is generally less.
▸ The reduction in spending by these households was less for bananas than for other fruits.
▸ Most money is spent on apples and pears.

### Consumption and expenditure for fats (per person per week)

| | Consumption 1992 (grams)* | Consumption 1993 | Consumption 1994 | Expenditure 1992 (pence) | Expenditure 1993 | Expenditure 1994 |
|---|---|---|---|---|---|---|
| Butter | 41 | 40 | 39 | 10.0 | 10.5 | 10.2 |
| Margarine | 79 | 70 | 43 | 10.0 | 9.0 | 4.8 |
| Low fat and dairy spreads | 51 | 52 | 74 | 9.1 | 9.5 | 13.2 |
| Vegetable and salad oils (ml) | 49 | 46 | 49 | 4.9 | 4.6 | 4.9 |
| Other fats and oils | 25 | 23 | 21 | 3.3 | 3.1 | 3.0 |
| Total fats | 245 | 230 | 226 | 37.4 | 36.7 | 36.2 |

\* Except where otherwise stated        Source – MAFF, *National Food Survey*

### — Task —

a  Look at the above table. What information do these figures give you?

b  How could this information be useful when designing and making food products?

*T*he extracts in Unit 4.2 from the Food Survey and Mintel reports are examples of secondary source evidence, because they were collected by somebody else. If the information is relevant to the task, it should be sifted to identify and select the points that will best help the development and success of a product. For example, if the task involves developing a product where the target market is families of two adults with two children, in income group C, sifting the information from the Food Survey would yield the relevant figure which shows that an average family of this type spent just over £10 per person per week in 1994.

## Task

1 a Sift the information given in the graph on page 92 to find out how much per person per week was spent in 1994 by each of the following household types.
  ▸ two adults, one child, in income group D plus E2
  ▸ two adults, one child, in income group A.
  b What is the difference per person per week between the two groups?
  c If you were involved in the development of a range of main meal convenience products for the family type in each of the income groups mentioned in a, how would you make sure that there was a product in the range which would be suitable for each group?

## Another example of sifting information

Suppose you have been asked to design and make a range of products which could help reduce the amount of fat in the diets of the playing members of a local football team. This would involve collecting information including:
▸ the energy and nutrient needs of this target group
▸ the main sources of fat in the average British diet
▸ the meal patterns of, and foods eaten by, a group of footballers who play in a local team.

The information in the illustration on the opposite page could help you in your research.

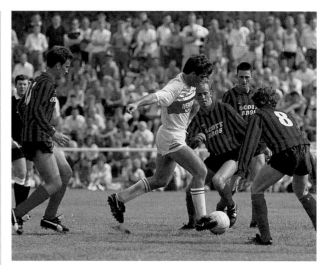
■ The target group

*How can you tackle a task like this?*
▸ Start by listing the groups of foods in order, starting with the group which is the largest source and ending with those groups which supply the least.
▸ Select those groups of food which are likely to supply the energy and other nutrient needs of this group, without too much fat.
▸ Identify some of the foods from the pictures of the food groups and consider how useful they might be as ingredients for dishes within the range.
▸ Check the nutrient needs and meal patterns of the target group to make sure the foods you have identified are likely to fulfil the needs and prove popular.

*Investigating the meal patterns of, and food eaten by, the footballers*

Primary research methods are best because the information you need is specific to the task. The best way of obtaining the information would be by interviewing members of the team. The interviews would need careful advance planning. Lists of the information required should be made, then specific questions related to that information can be written down beforehand. A response sheet could be prepared, to be filled in either by the interviewer or the interviewees (i.e. members of the team). Questions must be phrased clearly to elicit (find out) useful information.

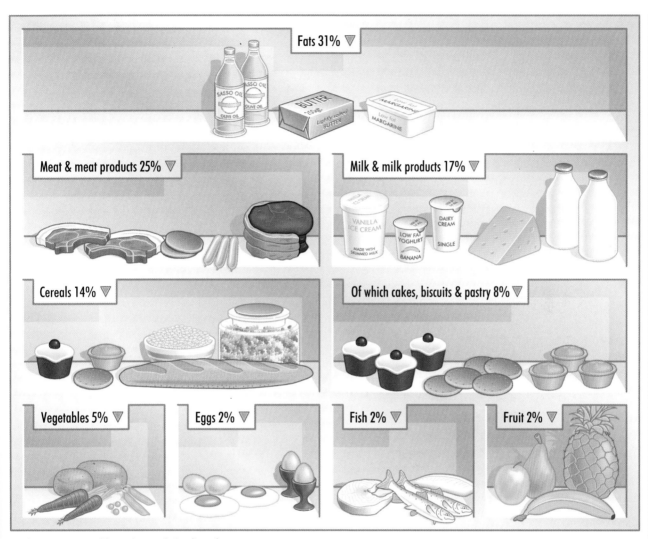

- The main sources of fat in the British diet (by %)

*Examples of suitable questions*

▶ How many meals do you have in a day?
▶ At what times of day are these meals taken?
▶ Do you eat and drink between meals? If so, what types of food and drink do you typically use? In what amounts?
▶ Give an example of the amounts (i.e. portion sizes) of foods you eat for each meal.
▶ What are your favourite foods and drinks? Why do you like them?

The answers given will help you to identify:

▶ high-fat foods eaten regularly
▶ meal patterns and the degree of 'snacking' (Between-meals snack foods are frequently high-fat varieties.)

▶ individual understanding of portion sizes. (For example, portions of high-fat foods may be larger than is necessary or desirable.)

— **Task**

2 **a** Add to the above list any other questions which you think are relevant to the task.
**b** Prepare a question and answer sheet in preparation for the interviews. Use a computer program to help, if there is one available.

## What is a design specification?

A design specification contains all the information about the product or products which will meet the requirements of the task. In the football team example discussed in Unit 4.3, the main requirements are:
▶ reduced-fat products
▶ high-energy products (to fit the activity level of the target group)
▶ products acceptable to the target group in terms of enjoyment and life-style constraints or opportunities.

The design specification must include details of:
▶ types of foods (e.g. high-energy foods such as pasta, potatoes, bread; foods high in protein, low in fat e.g. lean meat, chicken, fish, including oily fish)
▶ appropriate combinations of food to meet food choices identified in the research
▶ portion sizes
▶ suitable dishes
▶ range offered.

This type of specification is used to develop specific products to meet the requirements of the task. Ideas for products are measured against that specification to make sure they fulfil the needs of the target group. If it is decided that a product idea is appropriate a detailed specification for its production will be made. This specification must contain:
▶ precise reference to amounts and types of each ingredient (the recipe or formulation) and the ratio of each ingredient to the others
▶ serving size
▶ processing details
▶ precise descriptions of sensory, nutritional and other relevant qualities
▶ precise reference to size, shape and presentation of the product.

## Using specifications to evaluate products

The detailed specification is used to evaluate the product or products during the initial production stage and, subsequently, when the product or products undergo periodic checks for quality and consistency. Each time evaluation takes place the products must fulfil the specification in every detail. This ensures that the same standard of product is being made. If, for example, analysis of the results of the football team research suggests that steak and kidney pie, made with puff pastry, is a favourite dish with a number of members of the team, an idea worth trialling could be a similar dish made with ingredients with a lower fat content. A good example could be chicken and mushroom pie made with filo pastry. This dish would meet the requirements because:
▶ chicken is a low-fat ingredient
▶ filo pastry is fairly high in energy without being high in fat
▶ the combinations of flavours and textures are very similar to the favourite product
▶ it could form part of a range of products, e.g. other fillings could be included to provide variety
▶ it could be marketed as a frozen or other type of convenience product (to fit in with life-style constraints).

## Planning product development

Next, a plan for the development of the product must be compiled. This plan is the same type of document as the process flow charts used in industry. The plan must include the activities involved, in the order in which they take place. Another name for this is a **time plan**. These activities could be shown in flow chart or block diagram form.

The plan must include details of the special points of care which must be carried out to make sure the product is of good quality, meets the specification and is safe to eat. These are the critical control points.

Some of the product flow diagrams in Section 2 show ways of presenting this information (see pages 13, 18 and 41). A chicken and mushroom filo pie product flow chart suggestion is shown opposite.

Making a one-off product, such as this pie, for trialling means that adaptations or modifications can be built in to the process if necessary. This one-off product is then an example or specimen, sometimes called a **prototype**. Judgements can be

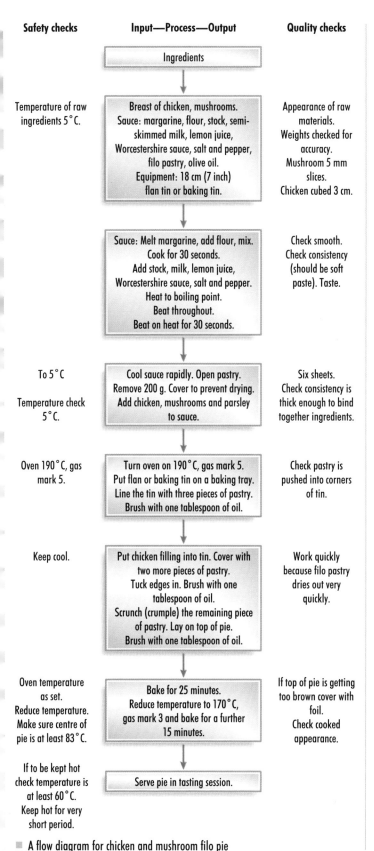

**Safety checks**

Temperature of raw ingredients 5°C.

To 5°C

Temperature check 5°C.

Oven 190°C, gas mark 5.

Keep cool.

Oven temperature as set.
Reduce temperature.
Make sure centre of pie is at least 83°C.

If to be kept hot check temperature is at least 60°C.
Keep hot for very short period.

**Input—Process—Output**

Ingredients

Breast of chicken, mushrooms.
Sauce: margarine, flour, stock, semi-skimmed milk, lemon juice, Worcestershire sauce, salt and pepper, filo pastry, olive oil.
Equipment: 18 cm (7 inch) flan tin or baking tin.

Sauce: Melt margarine, add flour, mix.
Cook for 30 seconds.
Add stock, milk, lemon juice, Worcestershire sauce, salt and pepper.
Heat to boiling point.
Beat throughout.
Beat on heat for 30 seconds.

Cool sauce rapidly. Open pastry.
Remove 200 g. Cover to prevent drying.
Add chicken, mushrooms and parsley to sauce.

Turn oven on 190°C, gas mark 5.
Put flan or baking tin on a baking tray.
Line the tin with three pieces of pastry.
Brush with one tablespoon of oil.

Put chicken filling into tin. Cover with two more pieces of pastry.
Tuck edges in. Brush with one tablespoon of oil.
Scrunch (crumple) the remaining piece of pastry. Lay on top of pie.
Brush with one tablespoon of oil.

Bake for 25 minutes.
Reduce temperature to 170°C, gas mark 3 and bake for a further 15 minutes.

Serve pie in tasting session.

**Quality checks**

Appearance of raw materials.
Weights checked for accuracy.
Mushroom 5 mm slices.
Chicken cubed 3 cm.

Check smooth.
Check consistency (should be soft paste). Taste.

Six sheets.
Check consistency is thick enough to bind together ingredients.

Check pastry is pushed into corners of tin.

Work quickly because filo pastry dries out very quickly.

If top of pie is getting too brown cover with foil.
Check cooked appearance.

■ A flow diagram for chicken and mushroom filo pie

made about its consumer appeal and quality, before batch or mass production starts.

The judgements can be used to ensure that the product can be made successfully and will meet consumer expectations. Further testing may be necessary to ensure that increasing the quantities of ingredients does not change the quality which has been achieved in the successful prototype.

In the chicken and mushroom filo pie there are two ingredients which have been designed and included by manufacturers to ensure quality of outcome and to give a high degree of consistency in products. The two ingredients are the filo pastry and the chicken stock cube, and are referred to as **standard components**. Using standard components saves time and helps ensure that consistent products are made. Other examples of standard components include canned pie fillings, frozen pizza bases and pastries.

## ▬ *Tasks* ▬

1  a  Identify and research the composition and use of a number of standard components.

   b  Use what you have found out during your research to give details of the advantages and disadvantages of using standard components in your designing and making work in school.

2  a  Choose one example of a standard component.

   b  Use it to make up a dish which would be suitable for inclusion in a promotional leaflet about the component.

   c  If you have a camera available, take a photograph of the finished dish.

   d  Write out the recipe and method for making the dish in a form that you think will best encourage consumers to buy the component.

   e  Present the recipe and method with the photograph (if you have one) as they should appear on the leaflet. Show them as part of the whole leaflet design for the promotion.

## During the making process

Checks must be made on timings, sequence of activities, instructions and the selection and use of tools and equipment for their appropriateness and for whether the qualities required are achieved. For example, instructions about size and shape, weight and volume must be clear, to ensure quality and consistency.

Textures, flavours and appearance must be checked and managed to meet the specification. For example, in the chicken and mushroom filo pie example, the specification states that the chicken must be boneless and cut into 3 cm cubes and the mushrooms cut into slices 5 mm thick. During the making process, these measurements would be checked. In addition the **viscosity** (i.e. degree of flow, thickness) of the sauce used to moisten the filling in the pie will be determined by the specification. This states the ratio of starch to liquid required to produce a sauce that is thick enough to moisten, but not so thin that it will run out of the pie during cooking. If the results show that the ratio stated does not meet the requirements, adjustments must be made and another prototype will be made to test the results of that adjustment.

All of the qualities defined in the specification are checked, and modifications are made if requirements are not met.

## Finding out what people think of the product

Most judgements about a product are based on the **sensory** qualities which it possesses. Testing products for these qualities is called **sensory evaluation**. The three main reasons for carrying out sensory evaluation are:
▶ to find out the opinions of consumers
▶ to check the effectiveness of specific processing techniques
▶ to check that a product is within its specification.

In the case of the chicken and mushroom filo pie, the opinions of the target market will need to be sought. The people chosen to taste the product should be typical of the target group. They become the panel. A simple way to monitor consumer reaction is to use a 'smiley' questionnaire, such as the one shown below. The round faces are the **facial hedonic scale**. This is one of the most commonly used evaluation techniques for measuring food preferences.

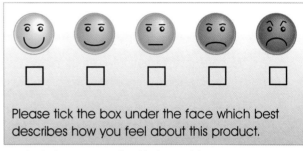

Please tick the box under the face which best describes how you feel about this product.

■ A 'smiley' questionnaire (facial hedonic scale)

Other examples of the hedonic scale which can be used include the nine phrases below:
▶ like extremely
▶ like very much
▶ like moderately
▶ like slightly
▶ neither like nor dislike
▶ dislike slightly
▶ dislike moderately
▶ dislike very much
▶ dislike extremely.

The phrases give more precise indications of consumer reaction but, for the purposes of the 'low-fat for footballers' brief, the 'Smiley faces' will give adequate feedback. To get more detailed information about whether the product would be eaten, another set of questions could be asked. These questions form a **food action** or **attitude rating scale**. A response form such as the one on the opposite page should be given to each member of the panel.

# Response form

**Name:** _____     **Product:** _____

**Attitude:** Tick the box which best describes your attitude to this product.

I would eat this at every opportunity I had. ☐

I would eat this very often. ☐

I would eat this frequently. ☐

I like this and would eat it now and then ☐

I would eat this if available but would not go out of my way. ☐

I don't like it but would eat it occasionally. ☐

I would hardly ever eat this. ☐

I would eat this only if there were no other food choices. ☐

I would eat this if I were forced to. ☐

## Task

a  Prepare a chicken and mushroom filo pie using the recipe below.

### Filling
225 g breast of chicken (cut into 3 cm cubes)
110 g mushrooms (cut into 5 mm slices)
25 g margarine
25 g flour
130 ml chicken stock (made with chicken stock cube)
1 tablespoon semi-skimmed milk
1 tablespoon lemon juice
1 tablespoon Worcestershire sauce
salt, pepper, 1 tablespoon chopped parsley

### Pastry
half a 400 g packet of filo pastry
3 tablespoons of olive oil

b  Follow the process flow chart on page 97.

c  Select a panel of tasters (a school sports team would be suitable)

For each member of the panel supply:
▸ a teaspoon
▸ a paper plate
▸ a glass of water (not too cold)
▸ two response sheets (One should be a 'smiley' questionnaire and the other an attitude sheet.)

Try to simulate the tasting booths shown and described on page 27, but note that coloured lighting will not be necessary for this test.

Give each member of the panel a small amount of the pie. This is the sample. The samples must be as nearly identical as you can make them. They must include all components of the pie. Tell the members of the panel to taste the sample and complete the 'Smiley' questionnaire and the attitude sheet you have given them.

Tell the panel members that they must not discuss their opinions until after the test is over.

d  Collate the responses. Analyse the results. Present the information in graphic form. Use a computer program if one is available. What are your conclusions? Suggest modifications to the specification if necessary.

e  Make suggestions for variations to be added to a range of low-fat filo pie products.

# Attribute analysis and other tests

Measuring reaction to products using the two hedonic scale measurements referred to in Unit 4.5 supplies evidence about consumers' opinions of one product. However, evidence is often also required about:

▶ what consumers think about one product compared with another or others, i.e. which one is best or which one is preferred. The tests used to provide this type of evidence are called **discrimination** tests.

▶ consumers' opinions of a particular sensory characteristic of a product. The tests used to provide evidence of this are called **descriptive** tests.

## Discrimination tests

These tests are used to find out whether there is a difference between the products used in the test. Two samples are compared at a time. There are several methods to choose from including:

▶ **paired comparison tests** where two samples are presented and the panel members are asked if there is a difference between them in relation to a specific characteristic. For example, which of two biscuits is the sweeter? Which of two pieces of meat is the more tender? etc.

▶ **triangle tests** where three samples are presented, two of which are exactly the same product i.e. they are identical. The panel members are told that two samples are identical and asked to identify the 'odd one out'. This is a very useful test when the differences between the two products are small. Sometimes panellists are asked further questions about the samples. The questions could be about a particular feature that either the odd one out or the identical samples have.

▶ **duo-trio tests**, again involving three samples. The panellists are told which one of the three is the control. They are then asked to decide which of the other two samples is different from the control.

▶ **taste threshold tests** to establish the lowest concentration of a substance which can be detected. Examples could include finding out how much water can be added to squash before the flavour is too weak, or how little salt can be added to develop an acceptable flavour in vegetables that are to be canned.

## Descriptive tests

These tests are used to find out about consumer reaction to particular characteristics of products. They include:

▶ **ranking tests** in which several different samples are presented and panellists are asked to put them in order of preference in relation to a specific characteristic such as flavour, colour, texture, odour. The ranking is usually done by code, for example if there are four samples, each would be labelled with a code or symbol, for example: ◇, △, ○, □. The tasters are asked to rank the samples in order of preference. Codes or symbols are used because people automatically rank numbers and letters, which could make the results invalid.

▶ **scoring tests** in which tasters are asked to make judgements about product quality, usually in relation to one characteristic. These tests give more information than ranking tests. An example could be the juiciness of meat, where the testers would have to rank each sample on a scale with descriptions which apply to various degrees of juiciness. The scale might be:

● extremely juicy
● moderately juicy
● slightly juicy
● slightly dry
● moderately dry
● extremely dry.

The same idea could be used to determine the crispness of samples of biscuits.

## Looking at flavour and texture profiles of food

During testing of a new product, attempts are made to analyse and define flavour and texture. This is an important aspect of **disassembly** or analysis of commercially-prepared products. On page 11 there is a simple introduction to this. The activity is called **attribute analysis**. Some preparatory training is required to analyse and define flavour and texture.

## Flavour

The four primary tastes are:
▶ bitter
▶ salt
▶ acid (sour)
▶ sweet.

They are detected by different areas of the tongue, as shown in the illustration.

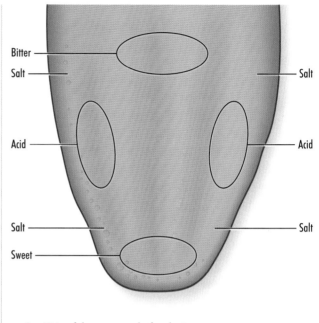

■ Sensitivity of the tongue to the four basic tastes

---

## Tasks

1 Work in pairs to do this task. For the samples you need:
   ▶ a teaspoonful of salt
   ▶ a teaspoonful of bicarbonate of soda
   ▶ a teaspoonful of vinegar
   ▶ a teaspoonful of sugar
   ▶ 8 wooden cocktail sticks
   ▶ 2 glasses of water.

   a One person tests their partner's ability to identify the four different tastes. This is best carried out when the taster is blindfolded. Cover the samples so they cannot be seen by the taster. Dip a cocktail stick into one of the samples. Ask the partner to:
      ▶ say whether it is acid, salt, bitter or sweet
      ▶ identify the area of the tongue where that flavour is the strongest.

   Carry on until all the samples have been tested. Record the results by writing the descriptions given for each sample.

   b Change over. Take a little time to tidy up the samples and change their position so that the new taster does not know which is which. Carry out the same activity. Record the results.

   c Discuss how accurate you were in identifying the different tastes.

2 Flavour is a combination of taste and smell. This can be proved in the following way, try it out and record what happens.

   a Peel an eating apple and cut it into slices.

   b Pinch your nose tightly so that you cannot breathe through it, and you have to breathe through your mouth.

   c Place a piece of apple on your tongue and chew it. Make a note of the taste.

   d Release your nose and continue to chew the apple. Make a note of the taste.

   e Compare the flavours before and after releasing your nose. Is there a difference? You should find that the flavour is 'deeper' and more intense when your release your nose.

   f Try the same test with a small piece of raw onion – if you can bear to!

   The reason why the flavour is more intense when the nose is released is that the odour which is passing through the nose joins with the sensation of taste.

# Texture

Texture can be defined by identifying the mechanical and geometrical characteristics and the mouth-feel characteristics of a product.

## Mechanical characteristics

Mechanical characteristics are the sensations which occur when biting and chewing food or moving it around in the mouth with the tongue. There are two types of mechanical characteristics – primary and secondary. In product evaluation a special vocabulary is used to describe these characteristics. This is shown below.

## Geometrical characteristics

These are terms to describe the size and shape of particles in the food, and how they are arranged. The following descriptions are used in product evaluation.

| Characteristic | Example |
| --- | --- |
| smooth | double cream |
| gritty | sugar crystals |
| fibrous | meat, celery |
| flaky | fish, flaky and puff pastries |
| cellular | mousse, Aero chocolate |
| crystalline | crunchy outside surface of a sponge cake or a Crunchy bar |
| pulpy | jam |

## Primary and secondary mechanical characteristics

### Primary

| | |
| --- | --- |
| Hardness | The force needed to compress a substance, for example, on a scale of 1 to 10:<br>1 — 5.5 — 10<br>marshmallow — peanuts — boiled sweet or Polo mint |
| Cohesiveness | Remains intact in the mouth during chewing |
| Viscosity | The force needed to draw liquid from a spoon onto the tongue, for example, on a scale of 1 to 10:<br>1 — 5.5 — 10<br>water — yoghurt — treacle |
| Springiness | The rate at which a mixture goes back to its original shape after being pressed with the finger |
| Adhesiveness | The force required to remove material which sticks to the mouth |

### Secondary

| | |
| --- | --- |
| Fracturability | The force with which a material breaks, crumbles, cracks, shatters, for example on a scale of 1 to 10:<br>1 — 5.5 — 10<br>bread — biscuits — uncooked pasta |
| Chewiness | The length of time needed to chew (masticate) a material before it can be swallowed |
| Gumminess | Denseness of a food, between viscosity and chewiness (usually a semi-solid, lemon curd is a good example) |

*Mouth-feel characteristics*

These are the sensations experienced in the mouth when food is eaten. They are produced by the water, gases, fats and oils present in the food. The following terms are used.

| Characteristic | Example | Characteristic | Example | Characteristic | Example |
|---|---|---|---|---|---|
| body | double cream | wet | water, drinks | tingle | fizzy or carbonated |
| cooling | peppermint | juicy | lemon, orange | | drinks |
| dry | water biscuits | oily | oils, mayonnaise | burning | curry, chilli |
| greasy | lard | waxy | chocolate | | |
| moist | fruit | slimy | peaches | | |

## Attribute analysis

=== *Task* ===

3 In this task you will take a product apart. This type of task is called **attribute analysis** or **disassembly**.

a Choose a chocolate bar product which has:
  ▷ an outer layer of chocolate
  ▷ a biscuit or crisp layer
  ▷ a soft filling.

b Record (taking information from the wrapper where you can):
  ▷ the total weight shown
  ▷ the description of the product
  ▷ the ingredients list in the order shown
  ▷ the price
  ▷ any other information (e.g. special offer)

c Remove the product from its wrapper. Describe the appearance of the product. Weigh it and record the weight.

d Take the product apart (no tasting yet).
  ▷ Chip off the chocolate layer. Put all the pieces together and weigh them. Record the weight.
  ▷ Remove the other layers and weigh them separately. Record the weights of each.
  ▷ Add all the weights taken together. How does the total compare with the weight printed on the wrapper?

e Analyse the geometrical characteristics of each layer. Record your opinions using the vocabulary listed opposite.

f Analyse the mechanical and mouth-feel characteristics of each layer by eating and testing a little of each. Do not eat it all! Record your opinions using the vocabulary referred to earlier.

g Does the product meet your expectations? Record details of your opinions of taste and texture.

h For whom is the product intended? In your opinion, does it appeal to the target market? Record details.

i How do you think this product was manufactured? Suggest the materials (ingredients) which may have been used to create each layer. What functional properties have been used? How might those materials have been processed in order to produce each particular layer? Record details.

j What critical control points and checks for quality would have had to be built in during the production? Record details.

k How do you think mass production of consistent products is achieved by the company who make this chocolate bar? Record details.

l Carry out stages **a–k** of this task using a product which competes for popularity with the first product you chose.

m Make a detailed comparison of the two. Use each stage in the task as a basis for the comparison.

n Use what you have learned about the commercial product as a starting point for designing and making a similar 'layered' product which could be marketed as a 'healthy' bar, appealing to those consumers who prefer less sweet products.

## More attribute analysis

Taking commercial products apart can often highlight opportunities for design-and-make tasks. Using this approach to design-and-make activities in school can ensure that concepts and their development are realistic and that they are likely to be achievable in terms of the resources available.

One example of a disassembly task which might lead to a design-and-make activity could be a comparison between two different commercially-prepared lasagne dishes, both available frozen. In an actual comparison, one of the dishes had a sauce on top which separated when reheated and as a result did not score well in terms of consumer preference. In Unit 3.2 (see page 66) there is information about how starch forms a gel when mixed with a hot liquid. When a sauce thickened by a starch gel is frozen there is a risk that the sauce will separate and weep (syneresis) on being thawed and reheated. Leading on from this, a suitable design-and-make task would be to develop products, such as lasagne, that contain a sauce which remains stable and smooth when thawed and reheated. Preparatory work for this could include short practical tasks where:

▶ other thickening agents are tested, such as cornflour instead of wheat flour; eggs and milk whisked together and gently baked on top of the pasta and meat layers prior to cooling, packing and freezing
▶ alternative toppings are tested, such as grated Parmesan cheese and breadcrumbs; skinned and thickly sliced tomatoes with sliced Halloumi cheese.

You could extend this task by experimenting with different ingredients. For example, instead of a meat-based filling, you could try a fish-and-herb-based one.

## Task

**4 a** Choose a cook-chill ready meal. Prepare it using the pack instructions.

**b** Record your opinions about the product by constructing a star diagram like the one shown below. This involves you in ranking on a scale of one to five all the characteristics shown in the diagram.

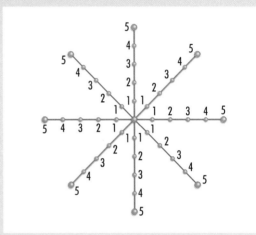

■ A blank star diagram

**c** Label the eight arms of the star as follows:
▶ seasoning
▶ mouth feel
▶ salty
▶ fatty
▶ initial bite
▶ moist
▶ sweet
▶ chewiness.

These are the characteristics of your chosen product. Rank them by marking the number which best describes your opinion of a particular characteristic.

**d** When you have completed all eight arms, join up the marks with straight lines. This will give you the particular star shape which describes your opinions of the product.

This provides a profile of a product and gives more detailed information about particular characteristics than other tests. The completed star diagram on the opposite page is a profile of two parts of one dish, a meat chilli sauce and a mixture of vegetables. The profile is very detailed because there are many characteristics covered.

e Study the diagram. Write a description of each part of the dish, taking your information from the characteristics ranked and the ranking they were given. For example, it is easy to see that neither part of the dish was fruity since the ranking for that is very close to 0.

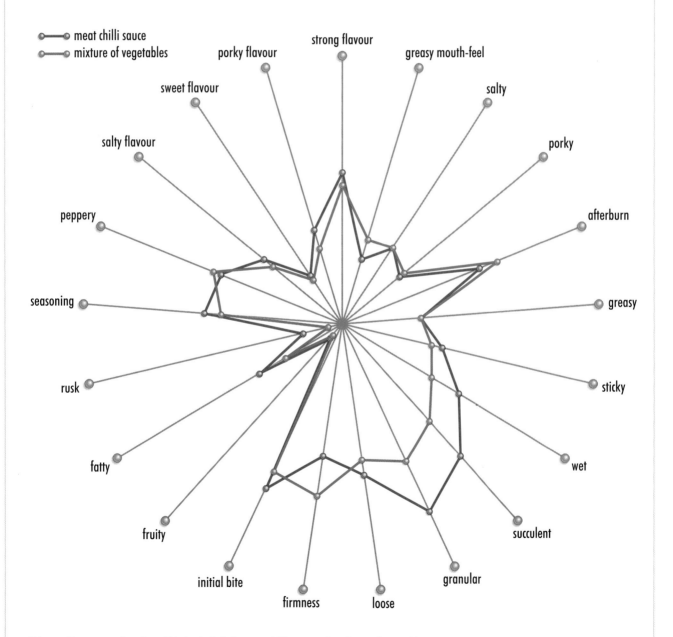

- meat chilli sauce
- mixture of vegetables

■ This star diagram was done for a dish that included a meat chilli sauce and a mixture of vegetables

## Using attribute analysis to investigate extending the shelf-life of foods

This is another situation where attribute analysis might be useful. Your starting point could be short practical investigations and tests analysing a range of preservation methods, for example drying, canning, pickling, jamming etc.

### Reminders about preservation

Successful preservation methods limit or prevent altogether the action of the enzymes and micro-organisms which make food deteriorate and become unsafe.

Unit 3.5 details the application and withdrawal of heat (see pages 84–5). These are the basis of preservation methods such as freezing, canning and bottling. In canning and bottling the food is heated to a high temperature which kills the micro-organisms. In freezing the temperature is too low for micro-organisms to grow. There are however other methods used when preserving food. They include:

▶ removing moisture – micro-organisms must have moisture to grow. When food is dried it is preserved for a long period of time. However, when dried food is hydrated, i.e. it has liquid added, it must be treated in the same careful way as fresh food, because its shelf-life is reduced to normal.

▶ making solutions – for example, micro-organisms cannot grow in:
  • strong acid solutions, i.e. solutions with a low pH, which is why pickling is an effective preservation method. The pH of the pickled solution is lowered by the vinegar
  • sugar solutions, which is why making jam, jelly and marmalade is effective at preserving fruits etc.
  • salt solutions which is why, for example hams and bacon and beans have been salted throughout history to preserve them

▶ removing air because most micro-organisms cannot live in a vacuum. This is why foods which are vacuum-packed have a long shelf-life. Examples of this are products that are packed in high-density polythene pouches. The air is removed from the pouch and the product is heated to a high temperature. The ambient products referred to in Unit 2.2 are an example of this (see page 12). The polythene must be of a type that doesn't alter shape (buckle) during the heat process since the seal might be affected and this could put the product at risk. In industry this is called seal integrity. It becomes a hazard if the seal is broken anywhere.

This is a different process than that used in **aseptic** packaging. When a product is packed in aseptic packaging it is sterilized and then put into a sterile container. The whole is then sealed with a sterilized seal to make it airtight (i.e. this is an **hermetic** seal). The whole process is carried out in a sterile environment.

## ▄▄ *Task* ▄▄▄▄▄▄▄▄▄▄▄▄▄▄▄

5 In this task, you will be analysing commercially preserved products.

  a Use different examples of how one product is preserved. For example, fruits such as strawberries are canned, dried and made into jam. Apricots are another fruit which could be used.

    Describe the appearance of the fruit in each case. Note any other ingredients which are mentioned on the label.

  b List two ways in which each of the preserved products could be used. Are any of the uses similar? Can one product be used instead of another for the same task? Give details.

  c In each method the fruit has been preserved but is the product the same in appearance, texture and flavour as the fresh product? Examine the appearance, texture and flavour of each – use the words listed on pages 100–3 to describe what you find.

  d Are there any advantages or disadvantages to the preservation methods you are studying? What are they? For example does this type of processing mean that a product is more adaptable in use?

  e Design and make a dish using one of the preserved products. An example could be a Victoria sandwich cake, sandwiched together with strawberry or apricot jam.

## Task

6 a Try out one method of processing to illustrate that preserving food prevents waste and extends the shelf-life of foods. You could do this using the following brief.

The manager of a local farm has more runner beans than can be sold in the farm shop. You have been asked to design and make a product which preserves the beans and presents them in an unusual way. The manager wants you to deliver a small batch of the product to test consumer reaction to your design.

The standards against which the success of your product will be judged are called criteria. The criteria for your product are as follows.

- The beans must be used in an unusual way.
- The shelf-life of the beans must be extended.
- A small batch of uniform products must be supplied.
- The product must be sufficiently attractive and interesting to stimulate consumers to try it.
- Suggestions for use must be included.
- Shelf-life information must be included.

Try the recipe below for your product.

b Deliver this small batch of jars to the manager. Display them in the farm shop. Check every seven days or so to find out:
- if the product sold well
- if it sold quickly
- if anyone returned to buy a second jar (having found the first one very satisfactory).

c Further checks could be made by, for example, leaving a short questionnaire which anyone buying the product could complete. Suitable questions could include:
- What attracted you to the product?
- Is it the 'right price'?
- Have you seen this type of product before?

## Runner Beans in Sweet Mustard Sauce

### You will need

6 jam jars washed and sterilized on a tray in the oven
waxed disks and clingfilm
labels.

### Ingredients

1 kg French beans
500 g onions
50 g garlic
2 rounded tablespoons salt
570 ml spiced vinegar (malt vinegar with 8 black peppercorns, 4 white peppercorns, 2 cloves, 1 cm cinnamon stick added)
1 level tablespoon turmeric
1 level tablespoon mustard powder
30 g cornflour
600 g demerara sugar

### Method

1  Top and tail the beans. Remove the 'stringy' sides. Cut into pieces 2.5 cm long.
2  Rinse the beans. Sprinkle the salt over them. Leave for 30 minutes.
3  Peel the onions and chop them finely. Peel the garlic and crush it to a paste.
4  Put the onions, garlic and 300 ml of the spiced vinegar into a saucepan. Bring to the boil and boil for 20 minutes.
5  Rinse the salt off the beans. Add them to a saucepan of boiling water. Boil for six minutes. Drain. Add the beans to the onion and vinegar mixture. Continue to simmer.
6  In a separate basin, mix the turmeric, mustard powder and cornflour with some of the remaining vinegar to make a smooth paste.
7  Add to the beans and onions with the remaining vinegar. Simmer for 10 minutes.
8  Add the sugar, stir until dissolved. Simmer gently for 10 minutes.
9  While they are still hot, put the beans and sauce into the sterilized jars. Seal each with a waxed paper disc and clingfilm top. Label with name, date made, ingredients list (in descending order of weight and volume), suggestions for serving, best-before date (this product will keep well for up to a year).

## Assembly line production

In the last task, if you were making the runner beans in sweet mustard sauce in a group of four, you could have set up a simple assembly line. This would give you experience in analysing and grouping the various tasks involved in the development of a product. For instance in the bean example:

▶ jars must be washed, rinsed and sterilized
▶ ingredients must be weighed and measured
▶ onions must be chopped, garlic crushed
▶ beans must be prepared carefully (to ensure uniform size) and mixed with salt
▶ onions, garlic and some vinegar must be boiled for 20 minutes
▶ beans must be cooked, drained and added to the onion and vinegar mixture
▶ turmeric, mustard powder, cornflour must be blended to paste with some of the vinegar
▶ the paste and the rest of vinegar must be added to the onion and beans to simmer
▶ sugar must be added, stirred and simmered
▶ product must be put into jars
▶ product must be sealed and labelled
▶ product must be delivered and displayed
▶ questionnaire must be prepared and delivered with each batch of the product.

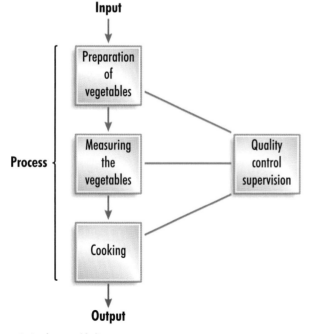

A simple assembly line

## Task

7 Work in a group of three or four.

a Suggest how a successful assembly line could be set up to carry out the tasks listed left. For example, you may need to alter the arrangements of the tables to produce a long surface.

b Plan each stage carefully. Suggest how much time each stage may take. List the tasks. One member of the group could be in charge of the preparation of vegetables, one of the measuring of the ingredients, one of all the cooking.

c Nominate another member of the group as the quality control supervisor. List the tasks this person must do. For example, check the size of the bean slices, make sure the times stated in the method are carried out, check that the jars are sterilized, that the 'workers' have washed their hands before starting to work and have tied their hair back etc.

d Set up your assembly line and carry out the task (or another task which you have chosen).

e List the parts of the process for which each person has responsibility, for example:
  ▶ The raw ingredients and their preparation is the **input**.
  ▶ The processing tasks are the **process**.
  ▶ The product (i.e. the small batch) is the **output**.
  ▶ The quality control supervisor in charge of **quality assurance procedures** and makes sure that a good quality product is being made.

## Quality control and assurance

Identifying the tasks each person is responsible for means that the whole team is part of quality control. In industry this enables any fault to be traced to a particular person (operative) who is carrying out a particular process or to a particular stage in the processing. It works as follows.
▶ Each task is identified in detail and each time the task is performed a form has to be signed by

the operative when they have completed the task.

▶ Each form usually has a code or number attached, which is used for every part of that batch of products throughout every part of the process (i.e. the **product run**). An example of this at Noon Products (see Unit 2.3, pages 16–20) is the checking and weighing of the spices which are added to a sauce for Chicken Madras. The operative has a list of all the ingredients, which includes precise references as to the form (e.g. powdered, whole etc.) and amounts. This is the specification for the spices which are later added to the sauce. The operative is responsible for the exact interpretation of the specification. In addition, periodic checks are made by a quality control supervisor to ensure the operative is carrying the task out accurately.

▶ Every time checking and weighing is carried out the operative must sign the specification form and put it with the spices as they move to the next stage in production. This tells the next operative in the assembly line that the ratio and amounts of spices delivered will give the correct flavour for that product. In industry this process is called **traceability**. It allows the progress of a faulty batch or product to be traced so that reasons for failure can be found and corrected easily and quickly.

## Tasks

8 Try this out with your assembly line production. Each person should 'sign off' when their task is completed. When the whole task is finished, you should discuss the success of the process. Notes for modifications can be added to lists, for future use.

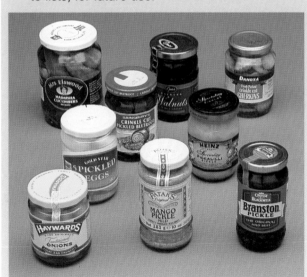

■ These products are likely to be the ones competing for shelf space with your large batch. How could this affect your marketing technique?

9 The manager of the farm shop is very pleased with your product. The responses to your questionnaire show that the criteria have been met. You have been asked to supply a large batch of the product. Explain how you will:
   ▶ bulk-up the recipe (i.e. increase the amounts but keep the ratio the same)
   ▶ ensure a batch of consistent products
   ▶ research sources of ingredients
   ▶ produce labels for the batch.

10 a Choose a 'pickled' product. Carry out an analysis of its attributes (attribute analysis or disassembly) by separating the ingredients into type. For example, pour the contents of the jar into a sieve, catching the liquid in a measuring jug. Sort the other ingredients into type and keep them separate.

   b Weigh and taste all the ingredients (components).

   c Prepare a star diagram. Decide on the relevant characteristics you wish to rank.

   d Complete the star diagram.

   e Produce a product profile description. This will give you detailed information to use when marketing your own product.

*D*esign-and-make activities can develop from a variety of situations, as well as the prompts and consumer needs which are referred to in earlier units. The next few pages give some examples.

## Example 1 – dietary guidelines

The following design-and-make activity arises from two recommended dietary guidelines:
▶ Enjoy your food.
▶ Eat plenty of foods rich in starch and fibre.

The buyer of foods for the delicatessen section of a large supermarket chain thinks that product development using vegetables would help to fulfil those dietary guidelines. The following brief is the result.

  The buyer of products for the delicatessen section of a large supermarket chain requires a range of three products, made with vegetables, that can be served cold or reheated according to consumer preference. The product range would be trialled during a promotional exercise with the title 'Eat Vegetables for Health and Enjoyment'.

  Design and make three products which meet the needs of the buyer.

### 1 *What will this activity entail?*

This puts you in the role of designer and producer. The buyer is your client.

  The client's requirements, that is the criteria within the brief, must be analysed. This is often best done by underlining the most important features or the factors to be considered. In this case these are (remembering the five Ws referred to in Unit 2.6, page 46).

**Who?**    the client
**What?**   vegetable product: enjoyable interesting dishes which can be eaten cold (i.e. straight from the delicatessen counter) or reheated
**Where?**  supermarket delicatessen counter (with chilled atmosphere)
**Why?**    to encourage vegetable consumption
            to help fulfil dietary recommendations
            to provide vegetable dishes which do not require lengthy preparation (which often puts people off fresh vegetables)

**When?**   to coincide with a promotional exercise with a health theme

### 2 *What research will be needed?*

You will need to research:
▶ vegetable composition such as cell structure, nutritional composition
▶ types of fresh vegetables, listed in particular categories, for example:
  • roots – carrots, turnips, swedes
  • tubers – potatoes, yams
  • bulbs – onions, leeks
  • green leaves – cabbage, spinach
  • legumes (seeds, pods) – peas, beans etc.
▶ types of preserved vegetables – as frozen, dried, canned, pickled.

■ **Fresh vegetables**

■ **Preserved vegetables**

▶ the effect of cooking on vegetables. This will include the ways of controlling cooking methods to achieve palatable result (such as crisp texture, good colour and flavour) and nutritional value. Carry out short practical tests to investigate the effects.

▶ the difference between starch and fibre (non-starch polysaccharide (NSP))

▶ attractive combinations of vegetables to give good appearance, texture, flavour. One example of attractive appearance is a vegetable terrine with different colours of vegetables arranged in layers. Carry out short practical tasks to test out your ideas.

▶ existing products, for example, what is already available? What prices are charged? Test one or two for flavour, texture etc.

▶ consumer choices. What products are popular. Why?

▶ portion sizes. What varieties are offered.

### 3  Analyse the research

▶ Consider what you have discovered from the research.

■ A typical delicatessen counter with some vegetable dishes

▶ List the points which stand out as relevant and those which will act as prompts for particular product ideas. Check these against the five Ws to see if they will meet those criteria.

▶ Draw up some initial ideas. Try to think of more than you need (i.e. more than three). Model these on a design sheet to give you an idea of the appearance, texture and combinations.

### 4  Choose final products

▶ List recipe formulations, processing methods, health, safety and quality controls which must be applied.

▶ Set a specification for production.

### 5  Set a specification

Set a specification for the development of a product range. Match this against the five Ws, i.e. the client's needs.

### 6  Put it together

▶ Make a product flow chart for each choice.

▶ Make up prototypes of the three products you have chosen.

▶ Set up a tasting panel. Carry out a ranking test to cover the flavour, texture, and colour of each product. Record opinions. Use the information about ranking tests on page 100 to help you. Collate the results. Write up your conclusions.

▶ Modify the products if the results of the panel indicate that the product requires changes.

▶ Make final decisions about the size and weight of each product, building in those tolerance limits of size and weight which are acceptable. For example you may decide a terrine measuring 10 cm by 5 cm would be acceptable within a range of 11 cm by 6 cm and 9 cm by 4 cm.

▶ Make and present one-off versions of the product range for the buyer to taste. Label them appropriately and according to legislation (see pages 33–5). Include a brief description of each product which shows how it will support the promotional theme.

## Example 2 – customer demand

This activity arises as a result of a discovery by the owner of a local pizzeria. Fresh yeast dough has always been used as the base for pizzas sold at this 'eat-in' pizzeria, but now customers are beginning to ask for different types of bases to be available. The owner has decided to extend the range of bases and also to offer a take-away and home delivery service.

Your tasks are:
- to suggest and trial two different bases with a variety of toppings (the suggestion is two versions of each base each with a different topping)
- to trial how pizzas made from the traditional bread dough and your two bases will have to be produced in order to provide good quality take-away and home-delivered products.

### 1 A *suggested starting point*

Research:
- suitable bases (e.g. pastry base, scone type mixture)
- topping ingredients and combinations
- other aspects including consumer choices, prices, portion sizes.

### 2 *Carry out short practical tasks*

Find out about:
- the various mixtures. Are they raised? If so how? Investigate to ensure success. Use a yeast-based dough as a control (to give you the standard you are aiming for)
- the various qualities which consumers expect from the product and how to achieve them. For example, how to produce:
  - the required degree of browning of the finished products
  - the correct degree of moistness
  - popular combinations of ingredients
  - a crisp base with a moist topping.

## Example 3 – a luxury product

A request to produce a range of luxury gateaux for a local restaurant gives rise to another type of design-and-make activity.

### 1 *The research*

The research involved here could include:
- identifying various types of basic mixtures which form the structure of most gateaux, such as whisked sponge types, rich pastry such as puff pastries, choux pastry, meringue
- finding out how these various mixtures could be varied in flavour and texture, for example adding chocolate, nuts, coffee etc.
- identifying various fillings, coverings, icings, decorations
- identifying the degree of risk involved in producing, storing and serving gateaux, including references to temperature.

### 2 *Practical tasks*

- Practise making some of the basic mixtures, fillings and decorations to become skilful.
- Find out which actions create a successful product and which do not.

These are some examples of suitable design-and-make activities. Each of them can be shortened to fit in with any reduction in time available to carry them out, for example instead of a range of products one product could form the basis of the activity.

## Example 4 – shopping trends

### 1 *The research*

- Analyse the messages in the article from *The Times*.
- Summarize the main points of the article. You may want to type these up and print them out using a word processor, if one is available.

### 2 *Practical task*

- What opportunities for future product development do you think might arise as a result of the main points made in the article?
- Choose one area where you think opportunities exist for products to be developed. For example, different recipe ideas for pasta, or healthy, interesting breakfast dishes. There are many other areas from which to choose.
- Use the area you have chosen for a design-and-make activity.

# Shopping for our food

### GILES COREN

Each British household spent £50.43 on food per week in the financial year 1994–95. £35.54 of that went towards meals prepared at home, £14.92 on meals out and takeaways. That £35.54 was spent largely in supermarkets.

Of that £35.54 domestic consumption budget, most was spent on meat and poultry (£8.04). £1.15 was spent on potatoes, and £2.86 on other vegetables. £3.40 was on cakes, biscuits and crisps, compared with £1.36 on fish, £1.80 on bread, 45p on pasta and rice, and £2.34 on fruit.

The British still get most of their carbohydrates from potatoes: 42.22kg each last year.

In the six months to May 1995 we ate 12,696 million meals; 28.4 per cent of them breakfasts, 21.4 per cent luncheons, 13.8 per cent teas (1.2 per cent down on 1981) and 19.6 per cent evening meals (2.6 per cent up on 1981), suggesting that we are eating gradually later and later. Snacking is down, too. In 1985, 19.5 per cent of all meals were snacks, last year that figure was down to 16.8 per cent.

Only 6.6 per cent of breakfasts involve bacon (consumption is down by half a kilogram per person per year, from a 1990 high of 4.45kg). And eggs are on the way out, too, appearing in only 9.5 per cent of breakfasts. Cereal features in 72.9 per cent of all breakfasts.

Potatoes feature in 41.3 per cent of all evening meals, compared with 21.8 per cent which involve salad. And nearly one in five of us eats a pre-prepared savoury dish.

We have continued to drink an average of 99 litres of milk a year – only the fattiness, rather than the volume, declining with the years.

Consumption of sausages has been one of the great consumer constants, showing only a very slight decline. In 1990 we were eating 3.55kg of sausage a year, and still consuming 3.17kg in 1994.

The overall impression is that our domestically consumed food is becoming more boring. The milk is getting thinner, breakfasts are getting colder, and we are stuffing ourselves silly with meat and potatoes.

## ━ *Tasks* ━

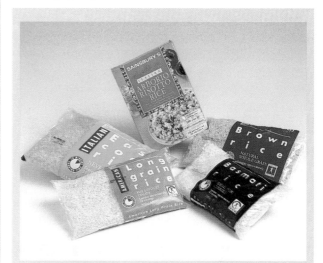

■ Different types of rice

1 a Choose one of the types of rice shown above and design and make two different products which show how versatile rice can be.

  b Write a short description of the rice you have chosen, include reference to where it is grown, how it is processed etc.

  c Using the two products you have designed and made, compile a proposal for product development to send to the company who supplied the rice you used.

2 It is recommended that most people should increase the amount of fruit they eat.

  a Design and make a range of sweet dishes using different types of fruit which would encourage people to cook with fruit.

  b Compile a business plan for setting up a small company which would specialize in the production of cooked fruit dishes to sell in small grocery shops.

# 5.1 Additives in food

*T*he production of a wide variety of foods which are safe to eat has been made possible by the use of **additives**. Without additives consumers would have to shop more often (because some additives lengthen the shelf-life of products) and they would not have such a wide choice of food. However the safety of additives is an issue in which most consumers are interested.

## How safe are additives?

Before they are approved for use, additives have to go through a long and strict safety review. If approved, they are labelled with an approved number. Additives that have been assigned **E numbers** are those which have been cleared as safe for use throughout the European Community. When an additive has been in use for a long time it is reviewed to make sure it remains safe to use.

## Safety tests

Food companies have to pay for any work, such as research and testing, which is carried out on an any new additive. This is very expensive and many companies prefer to continue to use permitted additives rather than research new ones. However, if a company does need a new additive, it must prove to the Government's Food Advisory Committee that the need is justified. Needs fall into the following six categories:
▶ to keep food wholesome and clean
▶ to fortify and/or enrich a food with vitamins or minerals
▶ to keep prices down
▶ to make a food convenient to buy, use and store
▶ to enable the food to be presented attractively
▶ to give a wide choice of foods.

A new additive is only considered if it shows advantages over those which already exist. If the need for a new additive is accepted, initial safety tests are carried out and the results are considered alongside any other tests which may have been done on the substance previously. These tests are examined by the Committee on Toxicity of Chemicals in Foods (COT). The COT may decide that an additive could be considered safe for a limited time, while further research on it is carried out. The COT also determines an **acceptable daily intake** for the additive. This is the amount which can be eaten safely every day for a whole lifetime without risk. This sometimes means that limits are placed on the type of food products which can contain the additive and also on the amount of additive which can be used.

The information from the COT is then considered by the Food Advisory Committee which advises the Government whether the new additive is acceptable. Consumers can register opinions during this process. Anyone can comment on the proposed regulations for the new additive and changes are sometimes made as a result of such comments. As mentioned earlier, approved additives are given numbers. When there is no E it means that this additive is approved in the UK but not yet by the European Union. Additives which do not have a number must be described by their full name on food labels. When most people speak of E numbers they do so critically, but is this criticism always accurate?

## What are additives?

Additives are chemical substances. Some occur naturally, others are manufactured, and are described as **synthetic**. Additives can be divided into groups according to the function they perform in food. They can alter:
▶ the sensory characteristics, for example, flavour, colour and texture
▶ the shelf-life
▶ the nutritional composition
▶ the physical characteristics.

Altering the sensory characteristics of food has become a necessary stage in large-scale food production because the consumer demands tasty and attractive products with good mouth-feel.

## Colour

In the UK in particular there is consumer demand for colours in food. In recent times consumer demand in the UK for bright colours in food has lessened but it still remains an important aspect of making a product attractive and to compensate for colour loss during processing. Caramel (E150) is the most commonly used colour. It appears on the labels of products such as gravy browning, soft drinks.

Other colours include beta-carotene (E160(a)), a naturally-occurring colour that is used in margarine and soft drinks, and annatto (E160(b)), which is found in crisps and fish fingers.

There is a group of dyes called **azo dyes** which have caused allergic reactions in some people. Tartrazine (E102) is an example. Tartrazine is used to colour some soft drinks. Some people believe that hyperactivity in children results partly from an allergic reaction to Tartrazine. As a consequence many producers of soft drinks have replaced it with natural colours.

INGREDIENTS: corn, vegatable oil, cheese flavour [flavouring, flavour enhancer (monosodium glutamate), colour (annatto, E160(b), sunset yellow, caramel E150), citric acid], salt.

■ The ingredients for corn chips containing three different added colours

## Flavour

Food flavourings are generally natural, such as herbs and spices. A great deal of effort goes into making sure food is flavoursome, both in the domestic kitchen and in industry. Different methods of cooking and combinations of herbs and spices are used to satisfy the consumers' needs for different tastes and flavours.

Flavours and tastes which can be achieved in food that is to be eaten straight away cannot always be repeated in the industrial production of food, so other methods are used to ensure that food is tasty and meets consumer demand. There is a part of the food industry which specializes in the production of flavourings. Flavour chemists experiment in order to identify the components of a particular flavour and, having done so, try to recreate the same flavour so that it can be used in processed foods. The chemist has to make sure that the flavour remains at the required strength and does not deteriorate during the processing stages of cooking, cooling, packing, storing and subsequent reheating by the consumer. Many of the flavours used are extracts from natural substances.

Research into flavourings has meant that many novel and interesting flavours have been added to food products and, in addition, any loss of natural flavour which occurs during processing is replaced. Examples include the many different flavours of crisps which are available.

Other products widely used to flavour foods are not actually flavours, but have the property of making other flavours stronger. They are **flavour enhancers**. Monosodium glutamate is very widely used as a flavour enhancer. It is often referred to as MSG (621) and is the salt of glutamic acid; it tastes salty. The Chinese have used this to stimulate the taste buds for centuries. Some people have suffered dizziness and sickness as a result of large intakes of MSG. This is sometimes referred to as Chinese restaurant syndrome. As a result, MSG has become unpopular. Some manufacturers now advertise products as being free of MSG, but the fact is that in proper amounts MSG is an extremely effective way of making savoury foods tasty.

The ingredients of a mouth-watering dish appear below, in two forms. Which one would tempt you? Remember they are the same dish. Chemical names are given to almost all substances to categorize them. The point to remember is that everything that exists is a chemical.

**Ingredients list 1**
Peppers, courgettes, onion, tomatoes, eggs, cheese, cumin, cinnamon, cayenne. Accompanied by a minted cucumber and yoghurt salad.

**Ingredients list 2**
Denatured proteins, polypeptides, amino acids, mono-, di- and polysaccharides, cellulose, cholesterol, linoleic, linolenic, arachidonic, lactic, propionic and butyric acids, oleic and palmitic triglycerides, lecithin, retinol, calciferol, phytomenadione, cobalamin, ascorbic acid, pisopropylbenzaldehyde, capsaicin and cinnamaldehyde.

Source – *The Chemistry on your Table*, Food Additives Industry Association

# Sweeteners

Sweeteners are used a great deal in the UK where a large percentage of the population demand sweet products. The two types are:

- **bulk sweeteners**, which give about the same level of sweetness as sugar. An example is sorbitol (E420), which is found in jam for diabetics and sugar-free confectionery.
- **intense sweeteners**, which give many times the sweetness of sugar and therefore are used in very small amounts. Examples are saccharin (E954), acesulfame (E950) and aspartame (E951), which are found in soft drinks, some yoghurts and sweetening tablets.

If a product is labelled 'low sugar' the sweetener used will be listed on the label. Low-sugar products are often targeted at the slimming market.

■ Two products containing sweeteners

# Mouth-feel and texture

During the processing of products certain characteristics must be developed. These include:

- consistency (viscosity), or the thickness or thinness of a mixture
- smoothness and stability
- a particular pH level
- aeration to produce a foam or raised texture and appearance.

## Consistency (viscosity), smoothness and stability

Emulsifiers and stabilizers (see pages 70–1) produce these required characteristics in manufactured food. They enable oils and fats to mix with water to produce smoothness and creaminess. For example, gum may be added to sauces where starch has been used to produce the viscosity required. The gum acts as a stabilizer and prevents the sauce from breaking down and weeping (syneresis). Examples of emulsifers and stabilizers include:

- guar gum (E412) used in packet soups
- methylcellulose (E461) used in low fat spreads
- sodium alginate (E401) used in cake mixes
- agar (E406) used in ice cream
- carrageenan (E407) used in milk shakes.

Many stabilizers and emulsifiers are made from natural sources. The best example of this is lecithin (E322) which is found in eggs and is also made from soya. Lecithin is used in chocolate products and low-fat spreads. If stabilizers and emulsifiers were not added to manufactured foods poor quality products would result. Foods where oil and water are components would separate out into fatty, watery droplets or layers.

## Acidity level of products (pH)

Additives which control the acidity of a product (i.e. its pH, see page 61) are called **buffers**. Examples include:

- sodium lactate (E325) found in jams and other preserves, sweets and flour confectionery
- calcium citrate (E333) found in soft drinks, UHT cream, processed cheese, dessert wines and ice cream. (The calcium can be mono-, di- or tricalcium citrate. They are all numbered E333.)

Acids are used to increase the acidity of a product (i.e. lower the pH). The most common ones are:

- tartaric acid (E334)
- citric acid (E330)
- acetic acid (E260).

## Aeration

Raising agents make it possible for a huge variety of baked goods to be produced. One example of a raising agent is E341, a raising agent found in cake mixes, dessert mixes and baking powder. Calcium tetrahydrogen diorthophosphate, calcium hydrogen orthophosphate and tricalcium diorthophosphate are all names used for E341. However, it is easier to remember the E number in this case! Another example is cream of tartar (E336), an acid-based substance which, along with an alkaline substance, sodium bicarbonate (or sodium hydrogen carbonate), makes up a raising agent which is widely used.

## ▬ *Tasks* ▬

1 Identify four different products which have additives included in their production so that their colour, flavour or texture meets consumer expectations. Name the products and the additives which have altered or improved the colour, flavour or texture.

2 Identify two different products with added sweeteners. For whom are these products intended? How does the sweetener additive make them suitable for these consumers?

## Preservatives

Additives which lengthen the shelf-life of products by making food safe for a longer period are called **preservatives**. They:

▶ help to keep food safer for longer, thus reducing the number of shopping trips needed

▶ lengthen the life of foods so that they do not have to be used immediately

▶ enable manufacturers and retailers to transport food in bulk, which is cheaper and can keep the costs of food down

▶ protect the food from contamination by micro-organisms, in particular bacteria

▶ increase choices in food because they make it possible for food to be available out of season and to be safely transported from other countries.

Preservatives are found in many foods which, without them, would have a short shelf-life. Examples include soft drinks, fruit yoghurts, processed cheese and fruit-based pie fillings. The preservatives used include sorbic acid (E200) found in soft drinks and fruit yoghurt, and calcium sorbate (E206) found in frozen pizza.

Potassium nitrate (E252) is found in ham, bacon and other cured meats. It preserves the foods and also gives them the pink colour.

Sulphur dioxide (E220) is used to preserve dried fruit such as raisins and sultanas, and is also

responsible for keeping their colour. This is an example of an anti-microbial preservative.

Another type of preservative is one which prevents oils, fats and the fat-soluble Vitamins (e.g. Vitamins A and D) from joining with the oxygen in the air and as a result turning rancid. These preservative substances are called **antioxidants**. The ones must commonly used include butylated hydroxyanisole (E320), called BHA for short, which is found in soup mixes, stock cubes and cheese spreads, and propyl gallate (E310), found in vegetable oils and chewing gum.

Other antioxidants, E306 to E309, are forms of vitamin E and are found in products such as sausages and cereal-based baby foods.

Continuous research into antioxidants is carried out in most countries to keep safety under review.

## Additives which enrich or fortify foods nutritionally

These additives include protein supplements, vitamins and minerals. Some must be added by law, for example, margarine must have vitamins A and D added. One of the main reasons for fortifying or enriching a product nutritionally is to put back nutrients which are lost during processing. Most breakfast cereals are examples of this. The ingredients list below is taken from a well-known brand of cornflakes, which is labelled as being fortified with vitamins and iron.

> maize, sugar, malt flavouring, salt, niacin, iron, vitamin B6, riboflavin (B2), thiamin (B1), folic acid, vitamin D, vitamin B12

## ▬ *Task* ▬

3 a Examine two different breakfast cereals. Note what is claimed and write out the ingredients lists.

b Consider the claims made. How are they carried out? The ingredients list and nutrition information should help you find out. For example if a claim is made that the cereal is low sugar, check to see whether sugar or sweeteners are included.

## Vegetarians

There are many reasons why people become vegetarian, including the beliefs that:

▸ meat consumption costs more in terms of the land that is used to raise animals for food than if the land were used to grow vegetables for consumption

▸ animals, poultry and fish suffer when slaughtered for food

▸ a diet without meat, poultry and fish is healthier.

There are different types of vegetarians, including:

▸ **lacto-vegetarians** who do not eat meat, poultry, fish or eggs but who will include milk and milk products in their diet

▸ **lacto-ovo-vegetarians** who do not eat meat, poultry and fish but will include eggs, milk and milk products in their diet

▸ **vegans** who eat no foods from animal sources, and use foods only from plant sources in their diet

▸ **fruitarians** who do not eat vegetables, cereals, pulses or foods from animal sources. They only include fruits in their diet. This is a very extreme type of vegetarian and people following this type of diet are likely to become deficient in nutrients very rapidly. It is unlikely that design-and-make activities will focus on this group.

## What must be remembered when designing products for vegetarians?

First of all it is important to identify the group being catered for. For example, when considering the vegan group, great care must be taken to include a variety of 'allowable' foods, such as nuts of all kinds, cereals, leafy vegetables and pulses.

The most important factor to consider when designing and making products for the vegetarian market is that when some food sources are removed from the diet, nutrient balance and quality may be lacking. The provision of iron in vegetarian diets is a case in point. Meat is a rich source of iron and if it does not form a part of food intake care must be taken to include alternative foods that contribute the required amount of iron to the diet. Adolescent girls and women can be at particular risk of iron deficiency (called **anaemia**) if they do not eat meat.

Cereals, bread, flour, potatoes and vegetables are good sources of iron and can be used as bases for products for the vegetarian market. Table 1 shows how much iron is provided per 100 g in some named foods. Table 2 shows how much iron is supplied in an average portion of the same foods.

| Table 1 – Iron supplied by 100 g of food | |
| --- | --- |
| *Food (100 g)* | *Iron (mg)* |
| Boiled lentils | 3.5 |
| Plain chocolate | 2.4 |
| Boiled soya beans | 3.0 |
| Steamed tofu | 3.5 |
| Tahini paste | 10.6 |

| Table 2 – Iron supplied in an average portion | | |
| --- | --- | --- |
| *Food* | *Portion size (g)* | *Iron (mg/portion)* |
| Boiled lentils | 30 | 1.0 |
| Plain chocolate | 50 | 1.2 |
| Boiled soya beans | 30 | 0.9 |
| Steamed tofu | 100 | 3.5 |
| Tahini paste | 19 | 2.0 |

When considering iron provision in vegetarian products, it is also important to remember that the iron found in plant foods is not readily absorbed by the body because substances present in plants, called **phytates**, reduce the absorption. This can be counter-acted to some extent by including foods rich in vitamin C, for example oranges, in the product.

## Single person households

The number of single-person households in the UK is increasing. Figures taken from Social Trends 1994 suggest that as many as 27 per cent were one-person households in 1994, with women over 60 years of age making up twelve per cent of this number. This means that there is an increasing need for food products to be available in single-portion sizes or small packs. But what makes up a portion? The idea of a portion differs from one person to another. When designing and making products, it is important to apply knowledge of what average portion sizes are. If there is too

■ Single portions of food

much, either food may be wasted or people would get used to eating too much and put their health at risk. If there is too little the product will not be popular because it will not be regarded as good value for money. Table 3 gives some examples of average single-portion sizes.

Table 3

| Food | Average portion (g) |
| --- | --- |
| Chicken casserole, medium average | 260 |
| Bolognese sauce, medium average | 40 |
| Chicken breast (without bone), medium average | 130 |
| Roast chicken, medium average | 100 |
| Ice cream, average scoop | 60 |
| Wall's Cornetto, mint choc chip | 75 |
| Cashew nuts | 10 |
| Honeydew melon without skin | 200 |
| Grapefruit, half, no skin | 80 |
| Taramasalata, 1 tablespoon | 45 |
| Prawn cocktail | 88 |
| Salmon steak | 100 |
| Tinned salmon in a sandwich | 45 |
| Cod, crumbed or in batter | 100 |
| 1 teaspoon low-fat spread | 5 |
| 1 teaspoon butter | 5 |
| Quiche small slice | 95 |
| medium slice | 140 |
| Soufflé | 110 |
| Pizza, thin crust, cheese and tomato | 116 |
| French beans | 60–90 |
| Brussels sprouts | 90 |
| Apple crumble | 170 |
| Cheesecake | 90 |

Other factors to consider when making food products in small packs relate to nutrient composition. If a food is a good source of a number of nutrients it is described as a **nutrient-dense food**. Bread is an example, particularly wholemeal bread in that it provides starch, non-starch polysaccharide (fibre) and many vitamins and minerals. Meat and fish (particularly fatty fish) are other examples. Fats and sugar have low nutrient densities because they do not provide a variety of nutrients. However, they are **energy dense** in that small amounts of each provide relatively large amounts of dietary energy. Current dietary guidelines recommend low intake of sugars and fats because, they provide dietary energy but few other nutrients. When mixed with other foods fats and sugars increase the calorific value of those foods. The examples in Table 4 illustrate this.

Table 4

| Food | kJ per 100 g | kcal per 100 g |
| --- | --- | --- |
| Boiled potatoes | 343 | 84 |
| Chips | 1065 | 268 |
| Fresh peaches | 156 | 34 |
| Peaches in syrup | 373 | 93 |

Care must be taken in formulating recipes for single-portion meals, to ensure that nutrient dense foods are included in an appropriate ratio. Products for very active people such as athletes, however, should have high-energy foods in a higher ratio because of their increased energy needs.

## Coeliac disease

People suffering from coeliac disease cannot tolerate **gluten**, the protein which is found in oats, rye, barley and wheat. This can cause damage to the intestine. Note the following points.

▶ Anything containing the cereals mentioned above *must be avoided*. This includes bread, flour, biscuits, cakes, many breakfast cereals and even those products which contain small amounts, for example sausages and stuffings made with bread.

▶ Maize, rice, cornflour, soya flour and potato flour *can be used* instead of the other cereals and in the same ways, for example as bulk or thickeners.

## Diabetes

People with diabetes have a condition known as **diabetes mellitus**. The condition occurs when the body does not convert glucose into energy properly. The substance that helps the body do this is **insulin**. Diabetes occurs either when the body produces little or no insulin, known as **insulin dependent diabetes mellitus (IDDM)** or Type 1, or when insufficient insulin is produced, known as **non-insulin dependent diabetes mellitus (NIDDM)** or Type 2.

When designing and making products suitable for diabetics, it is important to consider that:

▶ sugar intake should be reduced
▶ artificial sweeteners can be used, such as saccharin, aspartame and acesulfame K. These are available in sprinkle, tablet and liquid forms
▶ the same healthy eating guidelines apply as for the general population. In particular the intake of fatty foods should be reduced
▶ foods high in starch and fibre, particularly those which contain soluble fibre such as oats, vegetables, pulses and fruit, help to control blood glucose level
▶ diabetics should eat regular meals.

Diabetics should choose food carefully:

▶ to keep the level of glucose in their blood within the normal range
▶ to keep their weight within the normal range for their height or lose weight if they are overweight.

Particular attention should be paid to:

▶ carbohydrate intake, which should provide at least 50 per cent of a diabetic person's energy intake. The foods recommended for this are starchy foods such as bread, potatoes, pasta and rice, and high-fibre foods such as lentils, beans, wholegrain cereals and fruit. Cakes, biscuits and sugary drinks may be eaten in limited amounts, and foods and drinks sweetened with certain artificial sweeteners such as sorbitol (E420) should replace those which contain sugar
▶ fat intake, which should be limited to provide no more than 35 per cent of energy intake. This is because diabetics have been shown to have an increased risk of coronary heart disease (CHD). A high fat intake increases the risk of CHD

▶ the avoidance of special diabetic foods which offer no special health benefits and are costly.

## Allergies

Allergies are the unpleasant reactions to certain foods experienced by some people. In school, this issue is more concerned with making sure that foods which can cause allergic reactions are described clearly on the ingredients label and also perhaps by a special flash on the packaging. Nuts are one example. In this instance, the type of nut included should be noted because, for example, some people are allergic to Brazil nuts but not to others. Flashes could be included with messages such as 'Nut free' or 'Contains nuts'. Nut allergy is an example of a condition that can kill. The following case study illustrates this.

> A lady who knew she was allergic to Brazil nuts ate a piece of walnut chocolate cake and immediately felt her tongue swell and her throat close up so that she could not breathe. Luckily the people with her knew that she must be taken to the nearest hospital casualty unit immediately, where she could receive an injection (called an **antidote**) to stop the reaction. Afterwards the lady was very concerned that she may also have developed a reaction to walnuts. Since she had never before reacted to them, she made enquiries about the recipe used for the walnut cake. She discovered that the cook had added a small amount of Brazil nut because she did not have enough walnuts. This lady would have died if her companions had not known what to do.

### ▬ Task ▬

Identify a group of people who have special food needs. Carry out the following activity.

a Research and record the needs of the group.
b What opportunities do these needs provide in the development of a main meal product for this group? Note the opportunities.
c Generate ideas for product development.
d Carry out some consumer research to check your ideas are suitable and likely to be popular.
e Use the information collected in **d** to decide on a product or product range.
f Carry out a task or range of tasks involved in making your chosen product or range. If time permits, plan and carry out a full design-and-make task.

# 5.3 Pesticides

## Why are pesticides used?

Pesticides are used in the production of non-organic foods to make sure that food is safe to eat, more varied and available at reasonable cost. The use of pesticides is continually being monitored and is subject to strict controls on how much of each may be used. Legal limits are set which cover how much of a specific pesticide can be left in crops. These limits are called **maximum residue levels (MRLs)**. Meat, dairy foods, cereals, fruit and vegetables are covered by MRLs.

## Organic foods

Pesticides tend to have a bad press and many people prefer to buy food which is produced without them. There is a belief, too, that foods raised without pesticides taste better. This consumer pressure has created a market for **organic** foods. There are very strict controls over what can be described as 'organic'. These controls are national and are run by the UK Register of Organic Food Standards. These standards protect the consumer who prefers organic products by ensuring that the food is as it is described and is also safe to eat. There is a price to be paid, however, by both producer and consumer. The yield tends to be reduced and more waste results because some proportion of a crop will be diseased. All this, of course, makes for a more expensive product.

## Natural toxicants in foods

Foods grown without pesticides may also be at risk from damage or contamination from insects, rodents, moulds, fungus, soil pests and birds. It is a mistake to assume that all things described as 'natural' are automatically safe to eat, as many poisons exist 'naturally'. It is well known, for example, that rhubarb leaves are poisonous, so although most natural chemicals in food are safe we cannot take for granted that everything natural is harmless.

A relatively new area in which the Ministry of Agriculture, Fisheries and Food (MAFF) is involved are investigations into the long-term effects of natural poisons (called **toxicants**). As time goes on more information about the toxicity of natural substances in foods will become available.

Examples of foods which contain natural toxicants are listed below.

▶ **Dried red kidney beans** – the natural toxicants are called **lectins**. The beans must be soaked for at least twelve hours and boiled for at least ten minutes in fresh water to make them harmless. **Note:** tinned red kidney beans have already been treated and are therefore safe to eat without further cooking.

▶ **Green potatoes** – the natural toxicants found here are called **glycoalkaloids**. They are present in very low levels in all potatoes and in higher levels in the green parts of potatoes and sprouting potatoes (which should be discarded).

▶ **Mouldy dough** – the toxicants here are caused in moulds and fungi by **mycotoxins**. Moulds grow fastest in a warm, moist environment. Consumer pressure is towards removing the use of additives in bread, but without preservatives bread grows mould much more readily and quickly. This means the consumer must make choices between bread without preservatives which has a very limited shelf-life and bread with preservatives but which has a longer shelf-life.

## Hormones and anabolic agents in meat

Farmers are always trying to provide the type of product demanded by consumers and one which will make their farming profitable. In the past, increased meat production, particularly meat with more muscle and less fat, was achieved to some extent by the use of hormones. The use of these hormones has been banned for some time now, because it was discovered that in some circumstances they were a risk to human health. **Anabolic agents** are now used, in strictly controlled and regulated amounts and circumstances, to increase production and produce the type of meat demanded by consumers. The regulations and controls are designed to ensure that none of the anabolic agent is present in the animal when it is slaughtered (i.e. there is no residue).

# 5.4 BSE

## What is BSE?

For many years scientists have known that some diseases found in animals, both wild and domesticated, can occasionally be passed to human beings. Other diseases tend to be restricted within a single species, or a group of related species.

Scrapie, a sheep disease affecting the animals' brains, has been known for hundreds of years. So far as we know it has never affected humans. However it became the practice to use the remains of sheep in the production of processed food for other farm animals. This was done to make the best use of meat which would otherwise have gone to waste. The resulting food (usually in pellet form) was fed to cattle. This was intended to increase the animals' protein intake and raise their productivity during **lactation** (the period when they give milk).

In the late 1980s cows, usually in dairy herds, that were fed this artificial food began to show signs of a disease which was very like scrapie. They were affected mentally because the disease caused a change in the structure of their brains. This was a very serious problem and the Government instructed its scientists to research the new disease, which was called **Bovine Spongiform Encephalopathy (BSE)**. Cattle which suffered the disease were compulsorily slaughtered. By December 1995, something like 150,000 animals had been slaughtered and their bodies destroyed.

The research carried out into BSE showed that it was very like a human disease called **Creutzfeldt-Jakob Disease (CJD)**, named after the two German scientists who first identified it during the late 1800s. Until March 1996, CJD was thought only to affect people in middle age (50s plus). However, it became apparent that growing numbers of younger people were suffering from CJD.

On 20 March 1996 in the House of Commons the Government announced that its scientists now believed that there could be a link between BSE and CJD. This is still not proven and research continues. However, the inference drawn by the scientists is that, if there is a connection between the two diseases, then it crosses over between cattle and humans through the food chain (i.e. by consumption of contaminated beef).

In 1988, when the seriousness of BSE was realized, the law was changed to prevent any animal material being used in manufactured foodstuffs fed to cattle, pigs, sheep and poultry. In addition strict new rules were introduced in abattoirs so that those parts of the slaughtered animals known to contain the agent causing BSE (known as a **prion**) are kept strictly apart from the remainder of the meat.

The incidence of BSE in British cattle has steadily declined since the introduction of the compulsory slaughter programme and the removal of contaminated sheep meat from the food chain. Cattle in herds fed only on natural vegetarian foods (grass, cereals etc.) have been found to be almost completely free of the disease. There remains much to be done in the research programme to eradicate BSE from cattle and – to prove beyond doubt whether CJD in its latest form is caught by eating contaminated beef. The effect on the British farming and meat processing industries has been very serious. Britain is not the only country that has experienced BSE in its cattle herds but it has had the most serious outbreaks of the disease in Europe as far as can be determined (as of summer 1996).

## Finding alternatives to beef

When designing and making products in school for consumers who prefer not to eat beef, there are alternatives which can be used. The obvious ones are, of course, other meats and poultry which consumers are accustomed to. Other increasingly available alternatives are venison and ostrich, both of which are low in fat and are well flavoured.

## Task

Research alternatives to beef, lamb, pork and poultry. Find out the:
- nutritive value
- types of cut
- use in product development
- availability.

## Is food poisoning increasing?

There is considerable concern about the incidence of food poisoning in the UK. This concern is based on figures for the numbers of cases which have been reported, usually by the sufferer's general practitioner. People are much more confident about reporting illness of this type than they were in the past, so any increase in figures could simply mean that more people are reporting their illness than before. However, whatever the reason for any increase, food poisoning cases exist in large numbers.

## What is an outbreak?

An **outbreak** is an incident in which two or more people are thought to have eaten the same food in similar circumstances and at least one of them has become ill.

A **general outbreak** is an outbreak which affects members of more than one private house, or residents of an institution.

## Are there any regional or seasonal differences?

The map shows that there are regional differences in reported outbreaks.

The graph shows that there were seasonal differences in outbreaks in 1992 and 1993.

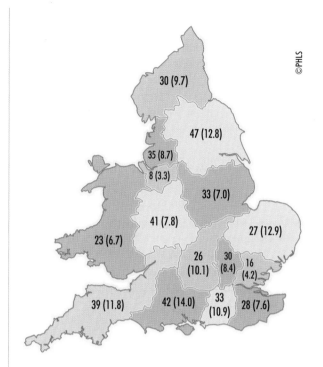

■ Reported outbreaks of food poisoning in England and Wales: numbers (rates per million population), 1993

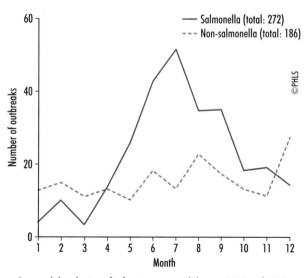

■ Seasonal distribution of infectious intestinal disease, 1992 and 1993

— Task ▬

a  Analyse the figures in the map and the graph.
b  Use a map of the British Isles to help you identify the regions shown in the map.
c  Write a conclusion which sums up the results of your analysis.

# Glossary

**acidic**   A solution or mixture with a pH between 1 and 6 (strongest acid being 1).

**additives**   Chemicals added to food, for example, to colour, preserve, stabilize or make food safe to eat. They can be synthetic or natural and are strictly controlled in use . Those referred to by an E number have been approved as safe by the EU.

**alkaline**   A solution or mixture with a pH between 8 and 14.

**allergies**   Unpleasant reactions to some foods experienced by some people.

**antioxidants**   Chemicals that prevent rancidity in fats – either by preventing the chemical changes which cause rancidity or by absorbing oxygen.

**aseptic packaging**   Packing a sterilized product in a sterile container, sealed in a sterile environment.

**attitude rating scale**   A scale used to determine what action an individual would take in relation to a particular product (e.g. 'I would eat this frequently', 'I would hardly ever eat this').

**attribute analysis**   Finding out about the method of production, the composition and characteristics of a product or piece of equipment. Sometimes called disassembly.

**audit**   A detailed examination of the composition of a product – often for a particular purpose, e.g. to find out how much fat a product contains.

**azo dyes**   Artificial colours, some of which have been linked to allergic reactions in some people. Tartrazine is an example.

**bacteria**   A group of micro-organisms, some of which can cause disease. Bacteria usually multiply by splitting into two, each resulting bacterium also being able to split in two.

**barker cards**   Large cards placed throughout a retail store, which advertise special offers.

**brand leaders**   Those manufacturers who are known particularly for certain products and whose product is usually the most popular.

**BSE**   Bovine Spongiform Encephalopathy.

**buffers**   Substances used to stabilize and control the pH of food. Examples include citric acid and tartaric acid.

**bulk sweeteners**   These have approximately the same sweetness as sugar (sucrose) and are used in similar amounts. Sorbitol (E420) is an example.

**caramelization**   The production of caramel by heating sugars above their melting point. Produces browning.

**casein**   One of the proteins in milk.

**cholesterol**   A fatty substance produced by the body and found in some foods.

**Chorleywood bread process**   The addition of improvers (usually ascorbic acid) and vigorous mixing techniques to speed up fermentation in bread production.

**closed loop**   A system where actions within that system provide information which enables the rest of the system (or part of it) to work efficiently. The information is called feedback.

**coeliac disease**   Where people cannot tolerate gluten, the protein found in oats, rye, barley and wheat.

**complementary action of protein**   When a protein is low in an indispensable amino acid (i.e. has a low biological value) it is said to be limited by that amino acid. If another food which contains the limiting amino acid is eaten at the same meal, the biological value is raised. This is known as the complementary action of proteins.

**concentration**   The amount of a solute dissolved in a specified amount of a solvent or a solution.

**consistent product**   A product that is the same quality, shape, size, texture regardless of the number made.

**criteria**   The requirements or characteristics of a task or a product that must be achieved.

**Critical Control Points (CCPs)**   The stages in a system where a risk exists or a hazard could occur. These stages are controlled by specific actions to be carried out at the point where the risk exists and where there is a potential hazard.

**denaturation**   The breaking or uncoiling of protein chains, caused by heat or by a change in pH.

**dextrinization**   The breakdown (or changing) of starch to dextrin. Examples include the browning that occurs when bread is toasted.

**Dietary Reference Values (DRVs)**   Estimates of the nutrient requirements of different groups of people. The values are guidelines for groups of people, not individuals.

**disaccharides**   Sugars such as sucrose and maltose, formed by the combination of two monosaccharides.

**disassembly**   Taking something apart to discover what it is made of, how it was made, the ratio of one element to another, in order to discover the processes used to produce the qualities it possesses. Sometimes called attribute analysis.

**duo-trio tests**   These involve three samples, one of which is a control. Testers are asked to identify which of the remaining two samples differs from the control.

**E numbers**   Additives that have been approved as safe by the European Union (e.g. E412).

**emulsifying agents**   Substances that enable stable emulsions to be produced. Examples include glyceryl monostearate (GMS) and lecithin.

**Enzymic browning**   This occurs on the cut surfaces of some fruits. Oxygen in the air reacts with enzymes in the fruits and causes browning on the cut surface.

**Estimated Average Requirements (EARs)**   Values that have been calculated for energy (or nutrient) requirements for groups of people. These values represent the needs of most people in a particular group. The EARs for energy are based on the current activity levels of different groups within the UK.

**facial hedonic scale**   Sometimes called the 'smiley' questionnaire. It consists of 5, 7 or 9 faces depicting varying degrees of pleasure and displeasure. Used in the sensory evaluation of food products.

**feedback**   Information gathered about the effectiveness of and demands made on a system, which is then used to enhance the effectiveness of the stages (or sub-systems) within that system.

**fixed costs**   Those production costs that do not change when the quantity produced changes.

**flavour enhancers**   Substances which make other flavours stronger, for example MSG (monosodium glutamate).

**formulation**   The ratio, type and mix of ingredients which form a recipe.

**functional characteristics**   Those properties of food that can be used to produce particular types of mixtures and food products.

**gliaden and glutenin**   Flour proteins which make gluten when hydrated.

**gluten**   The substance that gives flour mixtures elasticity, especially when strong flours are used.

**Hazard Analysis Critical Control Points (HACCP)**   The identification of risks and hazards at all stages in product development and processing and the formulation of control activities to eliminate or minimize the threat to food safety.

**high risk area**   The area in the processing of a product where the food is most likely to become contaminated with bacteria.

**hot-holding**   The time during which foods are kept hot – at a specific temperature – after cooking and before consumption.

**humectant**   A substance that keeps products moist.

**hydration**   Adding liquid.

**intense sweeteners**   Several times sweeter than sugar (sucrose) and therefore used in small amounts. Examples include aspartame E951, saccharin E954.

**inversion (of sucrose)**   The splitting of sucrose into the monosaccharides glucose and fructose.

**lactose**   Found only in milk, a disaccharide with about 16 per cent of the sweetness of sucrose.

**lacto-ovo-vegetarians**   People who will eat dairy products and eggs but not meat and fish.

**lacto-vegetarians**   People who will eat dairy products but not eggs, meat and fish.

**lead-in time**   The time between generating the initial concept for a product or range and the sample stage or the actual production of the finished products/s.

**lecithin**   The emulsifier in egg. Commercially produced from soya beans.

**life-cycles**   The period of time during which a product or product range remains popular and in demand.

**Milton Keynes system**   The production of pre-formed yeast-raised baked foods which are stable at ambient temperatures and which can be subsequently baked to produce oven-fresh products.

**modified atmosphere packaging**   Packing food in an atmosphere which is different from air. This often involves increasing the carbon dioxide ($CO_2$) level.

**non-enzymic browning**   a) the Maillard reaction between protein and sugars, sometimes referred to as carbonyl-amine browning, b) caramelization (the browning of sugar).

**non-starch polysaccharide (NSP)**   A mixture of polysaccharides (carbohydrate) from plant cell walls. A new name for dietary fibre. NSP is not broken down by enzymes in the small intestine. Some NSPs are soluble, some are insoluble.

**nutrition messages**   Information about nutrient needs and sources of nutrients and dietary guidelines for good health.

**organoleptic**   Affecting the sensory organs, that is: smell, taste, touch, sight and sound.

**palate**   Part of the mouth. The sense of taste.

**Parnut foods**   Foods for particular nutritional uses. For example, foods for people with coeliac disease.

**patent**   A legal document which shows that a particular process or invention may only be used by the company or person who was granted the patent. It prevents competitors copying the process or invention. Patents are registered at national patent offices.

**people and price points**   The pricing of a product at a level that the consumer finds reasonable for that particular product.

**pH**   A measure of acidity or alkalinity on a scale of 1–14 (1 = very acidic, 14 = very alkaline).

**plasticity**   Capacity of a fat to spread.

**point of sale**   Where the product is sold (i.e. where the consumer pays for the product).

**polyamide**   A type of nylon often used as a laminate which bonds onto another material to prevent the entry of oxygen into a container.

**polystyrene**   A type of plastic which can be made into trays and containers. It can be expanded and pressed into shapes to hold cartons etc. If is a poor conductor of heat and can be used for insulated containers.

**premium ingredient**   An expensive ingredient.

**primary processing**   The conversion of raw materials into food stuffs.

**prion**   The agent that causes BSE (Bovine Spongiform Encephelopathy).

**product technical approval**   Making sure that quality control procedures are effective and clear, and that processing techniques are appropriate and effective. Provides information about the specification, the flow diagram, hazard analysis and shelf life.

**profile**   Information about the purpose, target market, position on the market and personality of a product.

**prototype**   A sample product to be used for trialling and market research.

**quality assurance**   Ensuring that products are of good quality and are safe.

**quality assurance procedures**   Activities that monitor and verify that products reach the highest standards of quality and safety.

**quality control**   Stages and procedures during processing which ensure that products reach the highest standards of quality and safety.

**ranking tests**   Placing samples in increasing or decreasing order when judging specified characteristics, for example texture.

**recipe**   Sometimes called formulation in industry, it is the ratio and combination of ingredients required to make a successful product.

**Reference Nutrient Intakes (RNIs)**   The amount of the nutrient which will meet the needs of almost everyone in a specified group of people. RNIs have been calculated for protein, nine vitamins and eleven minerals. This amount of a nutrient will satisfy the needs of 97.5 per cent of the population.

**retrogradation (of starch)**   When water is 'squeezed' out from a starch gel. The reverse of gelatinization.

**scaling up**   Increasing a recipe formulation for bulk or mass production, keeping the ratio and proportions the same as the prototype or sample.

**scoring tests**   Used to evaluate food quality.

**secondary processing**   The production of food products from commodities after primary processing. For example, flour to bread.

**sensory testing**   Tests carried out to evaluate people's reactions to food.

**shelf-life**   The length of time a product remains safe to eat and of good quality.

**solution**   A solute dissolved in a solvent.

**specification**   The precise details of a product and/or a process which must be met for successful results.

**syneresis**   Liquid being 'squeezed' out of a gel when left to stand, or during storage.

**tainting**   The transfer of odours from one food to another.

**taste threshold tests**   Discrimination tests, to determine the lowest concentration of a substance that can be detected.

**tolerance levels**   The levels within which a process is said to be working effectively, safely, efficiently.

**traceability**   The method by which a fault can be traced back to the point at which it occurred, in order to remedy the fault and avoid it happening again.

**unsaturated fatty acid**   A fatty acid chain with one or more double bond. For example, when the chain has only one double bond it is called a mono-unsaturated fatty acid, when there is more than one double bond it is called a poly-unsaturated fatty acid.

**variable costs**   Those production costs that change when the quantity produced changes.

**viscosity**   The thickness of a liquid or a mixture, such as a sauce.

# Index